ONCE UPON A TIME IN CARROTLAND

MY YOUTUBE AUTOBIOGRAPHY
WHICH I DEFINITELY WROTE ALL OF

ONCE UPON A TIME IN CARROTLAND

JOSH CARROTT

Compass-Publishing UK

Once Upon A Time In Carrotland © Josh Carrott & Ollie Kendal

Published by Compass-Publishing UK 2021

ISBN 978-1-913713-58-4

Ghost-written by Ollie Kendal.

Ghost-ghost-written by Jenny Lee and Andy Brierley.

Ghost-ghost-ghost-written by a team of writers on Fiverr who cannot be named but specialised in erotic fiction. Ollie didn't know this when he made the order, but they were very pleasant and, to be honest, did a pretty good job considering the bizarre job they were tasked with.

Cover artwork © Ben Thomas 2021

Photograph of burning swan in Caterham Station is adapted from "A 4 EPB on the Southern Region standing at Caterham railway station in 1984." by Phil Richards

CC BY-SA 2.0 https://www.flickr.com/people/13035092@N00

A CIP catalogue record for this book is available from the British Library.

For Ollie Kendal, my best friend.

Contents

ABOUT THE AUTHOR

Joshua Daryl Carrott was born in 1988 and raised in Caterham, Southern England, and then Qingdao, Eastern China. It was at international school in Qingdao that he developed a love for Korea, having been befriended by fellow Korean students. He is married to Gabie Kook, and they live in London with their adorable dog, Brie. Josh spends most of his time making silly videos with his best friend, Ollie Kendal.

1

The Burning Swan

I have always felt that fairytale love stories are the deluded nonsense of a fanciful brain. Like in romance movies, where a man walks down the street, turns a corner and sees the girl of his dreams. Or a lady bumps into the love of her life while in a hurry and the only solution is abundant and unambiguous true love. In the first magical moments they sense that something truly incredible is about to happen. Their eyes twinkle, their stomachs leap and fireworks of emotion explode over the landscape of their lives. But in reality, these kinds of love stories are just fictional tales, and I do not believe they exist. I know some people claim to have experienced fairytale love stories and lived happily ever after, like the movie couples strolling into the sunset. Perhaps these people are born lucky. My mother is one of these people. I have heard my mother tell the story of how she met my father hundreds, nay thousands, of times, over and over until it has become woven into the fabric of my brain and etched onto the inside of my skull. Every family event is a chance for my mother to refresh our memories, and she always takes this chance. I know every word of the story, every tiny detail, about the one incredible, almost unbelievable event that changed their lives forever.

Growing up, I would always ask my friends about their parents' love stories. I needed to know if theirs could compete with my parents' epic tale of romance. As much as I do not believe in fairy-tales, it was always intriguing. I hurled questions at my friends in school and sometimes at visitors to our home.

"How did your parents meet? How did you meet?" They were surprising questions coming from a small but completely adorable child. It was never a competition, but if it had been a competition, my parents would have won the competition, every time.

Although my mother would not admit it, she was always keen to hear what they had to say and when they left, she would giggle and say to me, "Oh darling, their story was so boring. We totally won the competition."

To tell the story, I must first set the scene by describing my parents jobs, which were mildly interesting. Father was a firefighter, and Mother was a police officer. My mother's job involved arresting pesky miscreants and ne'er do wells. She told my brother Jordan and I how she valiantly chased pickpockets down the cobbled streets of Caterham in Southern England. My father talked casually about saving lives and heroically rescuing people and cats from burning buildings. Growing up, I wanted to be a police officer and a firefighter at the same time. A fire officer perhaps, or a police fighter. My father's firefighter suit and yellow helmet made him look like a superhero to me, but my favourite colour was police-black. My mother had de-escalation training and a walkie-talkie, which was seriously cool, but my father also had his fire hose and his pure fearlessness.

My parents' romance began in the summer of 1988, as the last of the apple blossom lingered delicately on the trees of the orchards. Caterham is best known for the East Surrey Museum which has a fascinating selection of many really old items of varying importance and a gift shop. There is Caterham Valley and Caterham on the Hill, and residents fiercely debate which is better. We lived in Caterham Valley, which is definitely better. Everyone there agrees. A lot of people commute into London from Caterham, as the train links are excellent and Caterham School is only a twenty minute saunter from the station.

Both of these facts make the bustling train station an unlikely setting for a story of true love at first sight.

Animals rarely walk down the streets of Caterham, but on the day my parents met, cries rang through the air that there was a goose on the loose. Actually, on closer inspection, it turned out to be a swan. The swan was first sighted close to the East Surrey Museum, crying out in terrible pain. It ran around, burning. Yes, it was on fire! At first, it was difficult to tell what it was. The fire had engulfed more than half of its body. It was like a moving ball of fire, knocking into rubbish bins and setting litter ablaze in its wake. Nobody knew where the swan came from or how it came to be on fire. Only time will tell.

It was a commotion that caused everyone to run for their lives. The swan ran to the front of the museum, which got people scampering inside for safety and novelty mugs. Quickly it found its way to the train station. This was where things got messier. Commuters panicked as the swan threw the railway station into pandemonium. There were cries and shouts of panic. Bowler hats and briefcases flew in every direction. The swan danced a deathly dance on the railway tracks, the beautiful white wings all burnt. It shrieked and moved in circles on the track, trying to take off. A firefighter came running towards it, wearing a firefighter suit and yellow helmet, and he had in his hands a fire extinguisher in case he needed to club it to death. As he was running to the swan's rescue, a police officer was also dispatched to the scene. Not understanding their intent to help it, the poor swan took off in alarm, hopping down the railway track. They chased the swan until it could no longer run and caught up with the sorry creature just as it collapsed on the track.

"If only we'd got here a minute sooner," the firefighter said.

"The swan was just too fast," the police officer answered kindly. "There's no way we could have saved it."

"That is true. I'm sorry, I didn't quite catch your name."

"Oh, I'm Maureen Smith. And you are?"

"Daryl Carrott."

At that moment a train came hurtling into the station and ran over the swan's smouldering remains. My parent's romance was kindled as the glowing embers hovered gently on the breeze like confetti.

An unlikely photo taken of the burning swan in Caterham, 1988.

And that is the story of how my parents met. The way my mother tells it is incredibly romantic, as if it was anyone's dream come true, except the swan's, of course. She always had a way of making things look bigger than they really were.

She would say things like, "Josh, sweetums, the bathroom is overflowing with water." I would run to check, and there would be only a few tiny drips on the tiles. No cause for alarm!

My father's account of their romance was more straightforward.

"Oh well, it was love at first sight," he would say. "We met each other on a job and we knew we were destined to be together. The stars aligned, the planets reversed their orbits, the moon eclipsed the sun and the birds flew south for the winter."

Like my mother always said:

"You can tell a lot about a person by the way they react to a burning swan." She is so wise.

"It did not take long to realise we were meant to be together, Josh, my little possum. He asked me out on a date and we met up again the very next day. Your father sure knows how to treat a lady right. In those few weeks of getting to know your father, I felt like I had known him all my life. A month later, he got down on one knee and proposed. He wasn't planning to, it was an irresistible impulse of the moment. He was actually reaching for a jar of jam, but ever one to avoid getting in a pickle, he asked for my hand and our relationship was preserved. It was strawberry, if I recall."

A year after they got married, they were blessed with a beautiful baby boy. I was born on the 14th of May, the same date that the famous Salem witch trials began in the United States, just 297 years earlier.

2

"Mutant Baby Will Destroy Us All!"

My life's first achievement was at the moment of my birth. I weighed twenty-two pounds and nine ounces, which was and still is a world record. I remain the heaviest baby ever born to this day. When my mother was pregnant with me, her belly was so big she feared she had a whole pack of babies in her belly.

"How many are in here?!" she cried out to my father.

Her weight doubled, and then tripled and even noncupled. It was almost unbelievable. Of course my father was there for her like the firefighting hero he was, and he assured her all would be well.

"If I stand by you and you stand by me," he said. "What I mean is, if we stand next to each other, we can raise this herd of children together."

But it turned out to be only one colossal baby. I got delivered by a caesarean section at the East Surrey Hospital.

My birth left everyone at the East Surrey Hospital speechless. The doctor felt privileged to have witnessed a medical marvel and he insisted on conducting a myriad of tests on my mother. He wondered whether she was a new evolution of the human race, a superhuman, or perhaps I was. But the tests came out normal. There was nothing they could detect that explained why I was so big. It was just a phenomenal phenomenon. News spread throughout the hospital, and all the staff wanted to see the gigantic baby and his mother. There was always a crowd of admiring people who surrounded us whenever she walked around the hospital with me in her arms like a pile of breeze blocks. But they didn't have to get too close, I could be seen for miles.

"How did he get so big?" they asked.

"Nobody knows," my mother would say. "I ate nothing special, just the usual diet of exclusively root vegetables and root beer."

There was significant media interest in my birth and a photographer from the local paper, The Caterham Chronicle, asked for a snap of the gorgeous baby. I looked completely adorable squashed into my crib, but my parents were a little disappointed when they saw my chubby cheeks and gleaming eyes in the paper the following day, under the headline 'MUTANT BABY WILL DESTROY US ALL!

"How very dare they?!" she shouted! She wanted to sue the newspaper, but my father talked her out of it, and she let it go, reluctantly. My father secretly kept the newspaper and a few years later, when my mother had had time to calm down, he framed and hung it on the wall very close to the living room door in our house in Caterham. I always thought it was slightly too close to the living room door. It would have been better at the midpoint between the door and the window and at the same height as my mother's eyes.

When my mother found out she was going to have a baby, she bought many baby clothes in all different colours and many matching hats. Finding out that I could not wear any of the baby clothes was a blow. My giant limbs could not fit into the clothes, and my head was way too big for the hats. I had the biggest head for my age in the whole world. She kept the clothes, hoping the next baby could wear them, and it was such a relief for my mother when, down the line, my sweet little brother Jordan was born.

A few months after my birth, my weight dropped tremendously, which caused my parents to panic. They went back to the hospital and the doctor assured them that nothing was wrong with me. I was returning to a normal weight for a human child, but I was becoming exceptional in other ways. It would soon turn out that I had a strong, innate, intuitive and instinctive penchant for languages.

The Caterham Chronicle

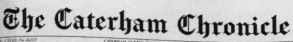

VOL. CXVIII, No. 46,353   CATERHAM, SURREY, SUNDAY, 14 MAR 1989   N   TUPPENCE & HA'PENNY

MUTANT BABY
WILL DESTROY US ALL!

JOSHUA CARROTT BORN WEIGHING A WHOPPING 22LBS 9OZ – NEW WORLD RECORD!

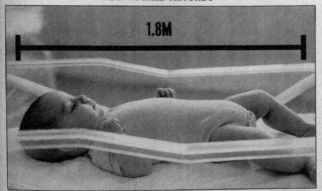

1.8M

Doctors at the East Surrey Hospital were left speechless Sunday night after a healthy baby boy was delivered weighing 22 pounds and 9 ounces. This collosal child is the heaviest ever born, leading to questions of whether he is a new kind of superhuman. It being only a year since the infamous "burning-swan-gate", locals are asking, has our sleepy Surrey town had a little too much drama of late. With tensions running high, all police officers in the wider Guildford area have been issued with swords in order to reassure the public. A local horticulturalist, mean Mr Allen welcomed the move saying, "Gosh darn it if anything else dramatic happens here, like say, I get an unsolicited call from a neighbour asking for gardening advice, I think I'll say something really really mean.

"It shocked me when I heard your first words, dumpling," my mother told me. "You spoke so well I doubted whether it was you, my sweet cherry-bakewell Joshikins. Your father came running down the stairs to hear his baby boy speak for the first time and, oh boy, was he struck agog, just like I was! It was not one word or two, sugar plum, they were sentences that rang out clear and true!"

"I'm hungry," is what I said, and it's regularly as true now as it was then. It's something I feel, more than once, every single day.

I gave my mother a tough time at birth, unlike Jordan. I was two years old when she became pregnant with Jordan, and she didn't even notice she was pregnant. Her second baby came as a surprise to everyone including Jordan. Although her belly did grow, in comparison to how it had been when she was pregnant with me it was negligible. On the morning Jordan was born, my mother had woken up with terrible pain. She thought it might be indigestion until she looked down and realised she couldn't see her toes.

"Maybe, I'm giving birth," she thought. While her first birth had been to a superhuman, the second time round she had a superhuman birth. She barely had time to come to terms with it when she sneezed and Jordan came shooting across the room like a rugby ball thrown by a professional footballer. Fortunately, I looked up from my incredibly tall LEGO tower in time to catch him safely in my arms, thus saving the day, my brother and my LEGO tower. From then on we were pals for life. I'm always there to catch him. My mother was overjoyed, and named him Jordan after the famous 'Air Jordan' running shoes, because his sudden appearance had made her jump. Jordan and I grew to love each other more and more and would jabber away to each other in what Mother called 'our secret language'. It was a language born from brotherhood, punctuated with occasional punches and pronounced with the tender timbre of affection. Speaking of languages, by the age of seven another one had caught my attention. I heard German for the first time on T.V. What I heard confused me. It was not English, but it sounded so good, so poetic and lyrical. I found myself repeating some of the words and that moment marked the beginning of a lifelong obsession with German. I replied to my parents in German whenever they spoke to me, and I asked them questions auf Deutsch.

"What are you saying?" my father asked.

"Ich spreche Deutsch, Vater."

"All sounds Greek to me. Where did you learn that from?"

"Das Fernsehen."

"I think you're making up words, sonny boy!" my father said. I was crestfallen. My first steps into language were squashed like ein Fehler (a bug). My father had no idea how much those words have haunted my life. These days I only speak German inside my own head, even when I'm in Germany. I've entirely lost my confidence about it.

Another thing I felt my parents did not understand, was my love for root vegetables. It all started when my mother bought some carrots from the farmers' market next to the meadow. She had heard about the amazing benefits of carrots, so she juiced them and she would give us carrot juice any time we asked. I kept coming back for more, and in no time, I had finished the juice of 45 carrots. Mother went to another farmers' market, the one by the babbling brook, and got some more. But I ate the carrots before she could grind them into juice, and she got really cross. She said she never wanted to see another carrot again. I felt the opposite, I wanted to see carrots, big carrots, big time.

3

My Imaginary Carrot Friend

On my third birthday, something crazy happened to me that I finally feel able to share with people in real life. I knew little about spirit guides while growing up, but one appeared on my shoulder when I turned three. A wise-cracking wise carrot that only I can see and talk to. His name was Muncho, and I met him on the morning of my birthday.

"Wake up sleepy head!" he said to me while I lay on my bed, asleep.

I wondered whose voice it could be. Could my mother have been whispering right into my ear? It didn't sound like my mother, or my father, or brother. It couldn't have been Jordan anyway because he was only one year old, and he was just learning his first words, like a normal child. The voice was tiny but piercing.

"Get up now!"

The words Muncho spoke to me that morning still shine in my memory, like balls of light that linger after you close your eyes having found yourself accidentally staring at the summer sun on a sunny day in midsummer. The voice was loud but friendly. I remember opening one of my eyes. It has always been difficult for me to open both my eyes when someone wakes me up. I flung my right eye open. My left eye needed more time. The room was pitch black, quiet and seemingly empty. With sleep tugging at my right eyelid, I shut my eye and drifted back to sleep.

"Happy birthday Joshua Daryl Carrott!" rang out a loud cry.

I felt something moving on my body. I sprung out of my bed in fear and lit the gas lamp beside my bed.

"I'm right here!"

"Where?!" I asked frantically.

I couldn't see who was talking to me. Was it something sinister? I was startled.

"Josh is three today! OHHHH…OOOOOOH."

I looked down at my shoulder and saw Muncho, a little orange carrot that talked. I was confused. First, I was hearing voices, and now I could see a carrot sitting on my shoulder. How did it get there? I picked him up and stared wildly at the carrot, this time with both eyes open. He grinned and waved his hands at me. He seemed friendly.

"I am Muncho," he said. "And you're Josh. It's nice to meet you." I was startled, and I couldn't move. Muncho started walking cautiously along my right arm.

"Don't be scared, I am not here to hurt you!" he said. "I am your friend and you are my friend. We are friends!"

I remember running to my parents' room, shouting.

"There is a talking carrot!" I yelled, half boggled, half excited. Wholly bogcited.

"Oh happy birthday Josh! You're three," my mother said.

"Mother! Father! Say hello to my little friend. His name is Muncho and he is a talking carrot."

"What little friend?"

"Muncho," I said. I pointed at Muncho repeatedly, but my mother looked at me with her weary but inquisitive eyes.

"Where is this friend you are talking about?"

"He is right here."

"Where?"

I tapped my right shoulder. They both stared at me.

"What does he look like?" Father asked.

"Like a carrot and he can talk."

They looked at each other, unsure how to react.

"Carrots can't talk," my father said.

"I know, but Muncho can," I insisted.

"Who is Muncho?" asked my mother, not getting it.

"Muncho is the carrot."

"Muncho is a carrot?" She was looking steadily more and more alarmed.

"You are not paying attention!" I was frustrated. My parents were being ridiculous.

"I don't think they can see me," Muncho said in a small carroty voice. "They can't hear me either."

"But why?" I whispered.

"Because I am your spirit guide. Nobody can see me except you. I am here to guide you through life's ups and downs, lefts and rights, tos and fros, longitudes and latitudes, and platitudes. I will help you find your destiny and help you fulfill any prophecies that may or may not arise in Chapter 23."

Muncho was right. It appeared I was the only one who could see him, and my parents were seriously unnerved. From then on I knew that Muncho was a special friend just for me, and that maybe nobody would ever understand that connection.

Muncho is a slim orange carrot with a leafy part on top like a green Elvis quiff. He wears white gloves and white shoes and has a friendly smiling face but no ears. He climbed up my neck and stood on my head to survey my parents' room.

My mother wanted to change the subject, so she brought out my birthday gifts. Receiving gifts makes me happy. I unwrapped them in a hurry, and my parents stood by and watched me warmly.

"What will it be?" Muncho whispered loudly with excitement. "A puppy? I love puppies!"

My mother got me a remote-controlled race car, and my father got me a Monopoly board game. He said I needed to understand how the finance world works.

The fact that I had an invisible carrot in my life that no one else could see or hear freaked me out and at first I didn't know how to react.

"You have us and your baby brother, Jordan," Father said. "You do not have to make up imaginary friends anymore."

I asked Muncho so many times. "How is it that you can talk? Trees can't talk, so how can you talk?"

"Oh Josh," he would reply. "I don't know. I am just a carrot. But we are going to have the best time in the world together."

Having a new friend was exciting, but I was distraught and sad no one else could see him. Muncho made me laugh and laughing alone sometimes made me look a bit weird. One time, at school, Muncho made me laugh so much that I was sent to the head teacher to discuss my 'inappropriate behaviour'. My parents were half frustrated, half concerned: wholly frusterned.

"Carrots DO NOT talk!" said Father again, when we got home.

After the visit to the head teacher's office, I had to be more careful. I spoke to Muncho in hushed tones and made sure nobody could hear me. I have learned over the years that people usually respond very badly if I tell them I have an invisible carrot on my shoulder. Muncho doesn't mind. He says we are a team.

4

PATRICIA FEATHERBOTTOM

When I was six my father brought home a kitten, which I named Patricia Featherbottom. I loved that cat, but Jordan would not go anywhere near her.

"Oh Jordan, my little cabbage, kittens don't bite," Mother told him, but little Jordan didn't want anything to do with her, on account of his lifelong fear of tails. When Patricia Featherbottom was a kitten, she would climb up to my lap and curl up, looking for warmth (I was the warmest child in Caterham). Patricia Featherbottom was brown with white stripes and she was beautiful, like a swan before its life is cruelly cut short by fire. Muncho loved Patricia Featherbottom too, but he feared her. Patricia Featherbottom could sense his presence. The first time I carried her, she kept sniffing and then she jumped on my shoulder, scaring Muncho who dashed for safety.

"Patricia Featherbottom can see me? Patricia Featherbottom can see me!"

Muncho's words were a mixture of fear and excitement: fexcitement. He was glad someone else apart from me could see him but it also scared him. Luckily there was little that Patricia Featherbottom could do to Muncho since she was only a kitten. I was the only one who played with her, which meant that whenever I was with her, Jordan and Muncho stayed far away. I remember once Mother bought me an ice cream, and then got mad because I shared it with Patricia Featherbottom.

"Josh pumpkin! What are you doing? That's disgusting!" Mother screamed. I screamed. We all screamed.

Patricia Featherbottom also slept with me at night, which worried Jordan and Muncho.

"Patricia Featherbottom can't stay in the same room as us," Jordan complained.

"She is staying on Josh's side of the room, not yours," Mother reassured him.

"But Patricia Featherbottom doesn't stay on Josh's side. She moves around like some sort of animal, and sometimes she touches my belongings with her tail."

I had no choice but to move Patricia Featherbottom out of the room so that Jordan could sleep peacefully at night. Instead she slept at the foot of our door, which meant we had to enter and exit through the window.

Muncho was upset because he wanted to play with Patricia Featherbottom, but Patricia Featherbottom was always scared of him. She ran off each time Muncho moved closer to her.

"But I am just a carrot, I could do no harm to her!" he cried out.

It was hard to tell if Patricia Featherbottom truly could see Muncho. She froze each time he stood in front of her. She would sniff and hiss and purr.

As they both grew older and bigger, Jordan took a liking to Patricia Featherbottom. Patricia Featherbottom also no longer ran when she saw Muncho. Instead she would groan loudly and chase the poor little ball of vitamin A around the house. It seemed that Patricia Featherbottom saw poor Muncho as an intruder in the house, and she was always on the watch for him. Nobody but me understood why she seemed to enjoy running around the house and knocking things over. And when I told them she was chasing Muncho, my father would look weary and ask why I still believed in Muncho at my age.

I got to see less of Muncho with Patricia Featherbottom always around me, which hurt Muncho badly. He was always in hiding and he missed me just as I missed him. Of course he missed me more because I had Patricia Featherbottom, Jordan, and my parents to talk to, and by now I was officially the most missable boy in South East England. The only time Muncho got to play with me was when he followed me to school and we had pleasant times together. But when we got home, he was out of sight.

We had never let Patricia Featherbottom out of the house for fear that she would run away, but one day we had no choice. Our house had become infested with hedgehogs, and the only known solution was to seal all the doors and windows and fill the house with crème fraîche. As this is toxic to cats we decided it was best to let Patricia Featherbottom out, but we were right to worry. She jumped onto a passing circus truck and we never saw her again, which was pretty ungrateful after all we'd done for her. But, as I always say, you've got to follow, follow, follow your dreams.

With the cat out of the house, Muncho and I got to have fun together again. There was a cartoon on TV every Sunday evening, which showed some children who loved to tend their father's garden. One day we decided it was time to have our own garden where we would grow our own root vegetables that only we could eat. We decided to call it 'The Secret Garden', but later changed it to 'Carrottland' for copyright reasons. My sudden interest in horticulture surprised my parents, but for me it was a way to get over Patricia Featherbottom. My father reluctantly agreed to let us use a small patch at the back of the garden.

"So what are we going to plant?" Muncho asked.

"Root vegetables!" I replied.

"And what are root vegetables?"

"They're a type of vegetable which, when you square it, becomes a whole vegetable."

"Really?"

"I have no idea. Let's grow carrots."

"YAYYY!"

We didn't know what we were supposed to do, so I asked my parents for help.

"What do you need a garden for?" Mother asked.

"Tom and his brother have a garden, why can't I have one?"

"Tom? Who is Tom?"

"He's an invisible beetroot who lives in my elbow," I said, chuckling.

"Oh dear, here we go again..." said Mother, concerned.

Then I explained that Tom was actually the little boy on TV who tended the garden with his brother. Jordan was not interested in helping me grow my garden, due to his lifelong fear of marrows. So Muncho and I took notes while watching Tom and his brother, and eventually we had a little idea what we were supposed to do. One thing we didn't understand was why everyone kept talking about beds. I asked Father why you would want to sleep in the garden, and he burst out laughing. Eventually he agreed to help Muncho and I to create our little vegetable patch, including beds. It was to be our own little corner of Eden, a fruitful paradise of vegetable abundance. Muncho looked forward to seeing a garden filled with so many carrots, but he got scared when my father said he couldn't wait to eat the juicy carrots from my garden.

"Why are we going to eat the carrots?"

"Because that's what they're for, Muncho, why else would I want to grow carrots in my garden?"

"But... but... they are just carrots, like me! Why would you want to do that?!"

"Carrots on earth are different from magical carrots like you, Muncho. You didn't grow on a tree, you came from a special place far away, like some kind of magical faraway tree, although for copyright reasons, let's call it space. There are other differences too. Earth carrots are paler orange and slightly longer, whereas you can talk, move, and breathe."

That was the reassurance he needed. There wasn't much Muncho could do in the garden, so while Father and I worked he spent most of his time playing in the mud and driving his imaginary tractor around. It was a tractor in his imagination, not in mine. I couldn't see the tractor and asked whether perhaps it was a spirit guide tractor.

Muncho laughed and said, "What a preposterous idea!" In no time we had completed work on the garden and we waited patiently for the carrots to grow. I'm not sure exactly what went wrong, but after months and months of waiting to harvest our delicious crop, nothing happened.

There must have been something wrong with the way we carefully cultivated our carrots. We went over our extensive notes again, but we couldn't tell where we went wrong. Then I remembered Mean Mr Allen who lived down the street. He had a bigger garden than us, and he had a lot of plants growing there. We begged Father to call Mean Mr Allen to help us with our little garden.

Mean Mr Allen was mean. He was the meanest meany in all the land. He refused, and told my father that he did not have the time to waste on kids. My father explained that we weren't trying to grow kids, but it didn't work. Then Muncho had an idea. He suggested that if I went over to Mean Mr Allen's and showed him my innocent face (by now the most innocent in the greater Guildford area), maybe he would reconsider. So we went to Mean Mr Allen's house and I knocked on the door nervously. The door sprung open and a hefty Mr Allen with an angry face looked at us.

"Who are you?" he barked meanly.

I was surprised with the question. I had known Mean Mr Allen for as long as I could remember. He had seen me around when I was younger. So why would he ask me such a question?

"It's Josh, sir."

"Josh who?"

"Josh Daryl Carrot. Surrey's most charming toddler, 1991."

Mean Mr Allen said really mean words to me and I cried all the way home. My father got mad and went over to confront him, but Mr Allen was so mean even my father and his fire hose couldn't reason with him. That closed the chapter on having our garden, which was this chapter.

5

MOTHER'S SWORD

Caterham was our home, and we had so many exciting memories there. My father would tell us fascinating stories of heroism and derring-do, which always sparked my imagination. Most of the houses in Caterham were made of matchsticks, so they caught fire a lot, and while my father never actually managed to save one, he always said it was a great way to meet people, and I realised that was something I wanted from my future career too. While my father was busy arresting the progress of fires, my mother was extinguishing the scourge of crime that blighted our safe little town.

Most of my friends' parents were lumberjacks and big game hunters, so my friends always wanted to know about my parents' jobs. The most frequently asked questions were: "Does your mum bring guns into the house?" "Does she allow you to hold her gun?" It is a common misconception that police everywhere are armed with guns. In England they carry swords. There was a time Jordan asked her if she brought her sword home after work, and she said no. We didn't believe her, and the search for Mother's sword began. We searched everywhere, from the fridge to the owlery, but for months we turned up nothing.

"Mother! Just tell us, please. We promise we won't touch it," Jordan begged.

"Swords are not for kids," she said, cleaning creme fraiche from the chandelier, and that was that.

Until one night, when Muncho ran into the bedroom, whispering at the top of his voice.

"I've found it! I've found it!"

I woke with a start.

"Muncho, it's three in the morning!" I guessed, as there were no clocks in the house due to Jordan's life long fear of time.

"I know, but I couldn't help it. I've found Mother's secret hiding place!"

"Where?"

"It was under a floorboard, just outside the armoury. I guess she never thought we'd look there on account of Jordan's life long fear of words that contain body parts."

I woke Jordan and we tip-toed downstairs, avoiding the haunted stable and the disused mine shaft that my parents had had installed to give the house character. We lifted the floorboard and stood there, looking at the box. We had never seen one before. I was breathless with excitement, but also terrified to open it. I didn't know what was going to happen if I touched it. What if I pierced a waterbed and someone drowned? What if I accidently cut off my own head, like Mr Petrov down the road did right after he'd criticised the Russian government?

"Should we try it?" Muncho asked in an awestruck voice.

"Try what?"

"The sword. I think you blow into the blunt end and pluck the sharp end with your fingers."

I sometimes wondered about Muncho.

At this moment my mother burst in like a water bed that's been pierced by a sword.

"Josh, dumpling! Jordan, petal! What are you doing, you naughty bunch of Carrotts? Did you touch it?" she asked, in a panic.

"No…" we replied, sheepishly.

Mother seized the box from me.

"I told you swords aren't for kids, unless it says so on the label. This clearly says 'Dry Clean Only'. Now I'm going to hide it again and this time there's no chance of you finding it. She took the sword away and hid it in another location where she thought we wouldn't find it, but after a few weeks Muncho found it stuffed inside a badger in the taxidermy room. Mother was less annoyed this time, and over the next few years 'Find the Sword' became a family tradition that we played on special occasions, and sometimes at school sports day. The kids at my school went in for very literal nicknames, so I became 'Josh the Sword Boy' for the rest of term. I liked it. It was the only thing anyone talked about until 'Long Limbed Larry' joined the school the next term.

6

Yuletide

One chilly winter, just before Christmas, (known more commonly as Yuletide in England), as icicles festively festooned our Caterham home for the final time, there was a particular incident that left us paralyzed with fear. I loved to decorate our house with Jordan in our own special Yuletide style. Although, my mother had strong feelings about the main Yuletide tree so she bought us our own little Yuletide tree. We hung colourful triangles on our tree, bouncy balls, Yuletide hats, ropes and muddy stones. It was diabolical, but we loved our tree, and that was all that mattered. Yuletide in Caterham was usually fun and colourful. Muncho loved Yuletide, but he did not like our Yuletide tree. Muncho thinks he is a talented designer, and he always has one thing or another to complain about. He never liked our decorations, and he kept on yelling at Jordan because he did not like the way he placed the things on the tree. And of course, Jordan could not hear or see him, which only infuriated Muncho more.

"Not there! Josh do something," his little voice would squeak. "Jordan is ruining our Yuletide tree!"

"Get over it, Muncho. It's Yuletide, for goodness sake!" I snapped, jumping to the defense of my sweet little brother who was trying his best to balance a muddy stone on a spindly and spiny branch. That was mine and Muncho's first major fight. He didn't speak to me again until Yuletide Eve when, for some reason, he forgot all about it.

Visiting Father Yuletide was one thing Muncho always looked forward to during the season. I don't know why he was always so keen when Father Yuletide can't see him. But Muncho did not care, and he made it a point of duty for me to take him to visit Father Yuletide. Visiting Father Yuletide when I was younger was so easy, but as I grew older, it became more difficult. Jordan stopped when he was six, but Muncho still wanted me to go with him even at nine.

"You know Father Yuletide is Mr Bombastic from church?" Mother asked.

I knew this, but for the sake of Muncho I said, "No Mother, Father Yuletide is real." When we got there Muncho would hop on Father Yuletide's shoulder and watch keenly as other children lined up to sit on his lap and collect their gifts. It was always fascinating for him and humiliating for me, but I'm a kind hearted guy.

Muncho's Yuletide wish from Father Yuletide was to have a companion. Muncho asked Father Yuletide every Yuletide to grant him another carrot friend, or at least root vegetable friend, who he could chat with whenever he was bored, and I was busy. Playful Muncho needed a playmate that was like him. Every year came with the disappointment that Father Yuletide had not granted his wish.

Except for Muncho's dashed hopes, Yuletide was always filled with joy and the Yuletide spirit. Yuletide carols were something we looked forward to at the Sacred Heart Church and I was soon given the award for the best mezzo-soprano caroller in Western Europe.

One Yuletide Eve, we got back home from the evening service a few minutes after seven. I couldn't be sure exactly. because we still had no clocks in the house, (because of Jordan's fear of time), and the clock in the car was late, but my parents never told us how late (again, because of Jordan's fear of time). Jordan and I could not wait to dance around the Yuletide tree, and I kept hollering at my mother.

"Open the door!"

We danced around the tree, our hands in the air, our voices loudly carolling, our spirits soaring, having the time of our lives.

That night, I had a very long conversation with Muncho, and we talked a long time into the long night. Muncho talked about how lame the Yuletide songs were, and I countered him. But just when I was about to give up out of sheer fatigue and concede that carols are lame, something I do not and never have believed, but I was young and had a lot to learn about life, just at that moment, I heard a sound. I turned on the lights. Jordan was asleep in the other bed. I got out of bed and peered out of my bedroom door. I was not scared because I knew I was not alone; I was with Muncho. As we walked into the living room, I heard whispers and scratching sounds. Someone was trying to pick the lock on the front door!

I ran to my parents' room and yelled at the top of my mezzo-soprano lungs, "There is someone trying to break in! Hurry!"

My crime-savvy mother pulled her sword out from under her pillow, and strode confidently out of the room while I stayed behind with my father. After all those games of 'Find the Sword' I was surprised that it had been under my mother's pillow, where any idiot could have found it or seen it sticking out. But thank goodness it was. I don't know exactly what happened, but my mother arrested the burglar. We did not speak about this the following morning, and never have since. I don't know if the reason is because it was so emotional for my mother, or because one crime blended so easily into her memories of the many crimes she had thwarted. Whatever the reason, I have learned to keep my feelings about it locked up tightly in a little corner of my heart. It's as I always say, emotions are for losers. Fortunately Jordan had slept through the whole event, which was fortunate because he already had a lifelong fear of burglars.

7

QINGDAO

Everything seemed so perfect in our little bubble in Caterham. We had our friends and neighbours whom we loved so much. We loved the matchstick houses, the cobbled streets and the apple blossom in the springtime, and of course, the practical and romantic train station. I had a childhood friend called Michael and we would play games together and talk about the goings on around town. We loved to go on walks, but we couldn't go far, cobbled streets are really hard on the knees. I didn't understand why we had to leave fair, green, sunny England. In 2004, the year I turned twelve, we moved to Qingdao, Eastern China. We left everything behind and went to live in a place where we didn't know anyone. Everything about Qingdao seemed new. The surrounding people were different from us in so many ways, they even spoke a different language and it wasn't even German.

My parents were excited about their new teaching jobs, and told us it was a new adventure for us as a family. But to me, it didn't seem as cool as fire extinguishing or crime fighting. My mother even had to return her sword and my father his hose.

"I want to go back home!" I would say to my poor exasperated parents.

"Oh Josh, my little apple-blossom-cobbled-street boy," my mother said. And that didn't help much at all.

A few months into our stay in Qingdao, Jordan seemed to have already adjusted to life in China, while I felt truly different and felt alone. I missed my friends back at Caterham. Jordan was excited about meeting new friends at school.

"How do you know you are going to make so many friends?" I asked him.

"I just know."

"What about Peter Piper, Georgie Porgie, Roger Red Hat, Jack and Jill and the rest of your friends back at home? Don't you miss them?"

Mother advised us to be open and to have fun.

"Maybe when you go to your new school, you will like it a little more. Jordan is happy here and besides, this house is bigger than what we had in Caterham, and it's even made of bricks rather than matchsticks. We'll have to put in a few features for character, but it's nearly there. I was thinking of a wishing well and a jellyfish aquarium," my mother said.

The house was the least of my problems. I wasn't happy in Qingdao. Three weeks after we settled into the house, my father thought it would be a good idea to go to May 4th Square.

"What's May 4th Square?" Muncho said.

"May 16th? I don't know," I merely muttered morosely.

Jordan didn't know what the square was either, but he was excited, anyway. He's always been the kind of person to make the most of massive life changes, and he'd recently conquered his lifelong fear of right angles. There was nothing at all special about the Square except it was astonishingly beautiful to look at. Jordan had brought two kites and he flew one up in the air. A graceful eagle in arresting golden hues. He begged me to join him with the other kite, a brown kite, but I was not ready to have fun yet. I was still sad and mopey.

"You know, it wouldn't hurt you to play with your brother," my father said.

"Jordan doesn't need me to have fun, he is having fun right now without me," I mumbled moodily.

"Just take the kite, Joshy peanut-brittle!" my mother said.

"But I don't want to!" My voice and my heart were mightily melancholy that morning.

"Apple-crumble-and-cream-with-a-cherry-on-top-and-sprinkles Josh!" Mother snapped.

Muncho appeared on my shoulder. He whispered into my ear and told me to take the kite and that I would feel better after. I took the kite from Jordan grudgingly. In that moment, to my great surprise I felt a spark of happiness spark from the halves of my flinty heart. The kite brought out the inner child in me (even children can forget their inner child sometimes). Soon, me and Jordan were having the time of our lives again. The May Fourth Square was the first of the many places we went to and I quickly discovered that Qingdao wasn't so bad after all. The people were friendly, and everything was just as cool as Caterham. Although I didn't have friends yet, that was bound to change, especially as I had already naturally picked up the language.

Jordan was excited to start school and he was positive that he was going to make a million friends in five minutes. The only thing he had to worry about were all the clocks on the walls, but he figured that if he didn't look at them, he would be ok. I was apprehensive about school. I had so many questions running through my head. Would my new classmates be friendly? How was I going to cope with an entirely new system, especially when Muncho was understandably so much slower at learning the language than I was? My questions were many, and my parents did their best to allay my fears.

"It's going to be fine," Mother said in her soothing motherly voice.

"Is it?" I whispered.

"Yes squishy Josh, it will," she motherlily soothed me.

"What if nobody likes me?" I worried.

"They will like you,"

"Why is that?" I whispered, hardly daring to ask such an emotional question.

"Because you are my son," Mother answered, "and you have the natural chatting talent that resides in our family genes ever since Charlamagne and Geoffrey Chaucer. Your brother has it too. All it takes is that you believe, believe, believe in yourself."

But still I worried. I doubted, doubted, doubted myself instead.

Just like every place in Qingdao, my new school was bigger than my previous one. My parents were with me on my first day, and my mother would not stop gushing over the size and beauty of the school. I think she was trying to convince me that it was a wonderful place, I think she also believed it too, but I sometimes find it hard to tell when someone's being sincere.

"The playground is huge," she said enthusiastically. "You will have enough space to play leapfrog and roll wooden hoops with a stick. You'll see, you'll fall in love with this place in no time."

The playground was big, and that boded well. I had always dominated playground politics. It was an international school, and I discovered that about seventy percent of the student population were from South Korea, which sounded like a magical place. My mother had told me that there might even be other students from England. Having someone from England in class might make me feel a little closer to home, even though I was hundreds and thousands of miles away. But it turned out to be Korean friends who took me under their wings and made me feel at home.

8

LEGUMASAURUS REX

The whole way through this major transition to life in Qingdao, Muncho was a stalwart carrot-companion. He encouraged me and made me feel so good about myself whenever I was down. He, at least, believe, believe, believed in me. He had, however, much to my horror and dismay, been joined by an imaginary arch-nemesis called Legumasaurus Rex, an organic dinosaur made of lentils, with no eyebrows. The lack of eyebrows sometimes made it hard to read his emotions, which could be disconcerting. Muncho's Yuletide wish every year had been to have another carrot sitting with him on my shoulder, someone to chitchat, chew the fat, and shoot the breeze with, whenever I was busy with my human friends. But Legumasaurus Rex was not exactly what he had wished for.

Legumasaurus Rex first appeared during the second week that we lived in our new house made of bricks. I was in the bathroom, trying to get yet another squirrel out of the U-bend, when I saw in my reflection in the mirror, the organic dinosaur sitting comfortably on my left shoulder. I froze. What was it? A lumpy dragon?

"Hello," he said in a deep, sinister voice. "I am Legumasaurus Rex, but you can call me Rex!"

I was not as surprised to see him as I had been when Muncho first appeared, but it was still a bit of a surprise.

"Where is Muncho?" I asked. Finally he might have another buddy, which would take some of the emotional load off me.

"Who cares?" he laughed in a way that I was not sure I liked. "I'm here now! RARRRRRR!"

Something didn't seem right about Rex. He could tell I was suspicious, he could probably smell it. I had a terrible fear that all was not well with my ever-faithful friend Muncho.

Rex stood up and danced around on my shoulders, trying to look cute, but looking sneaky instead.

"So what's up?" he said.

"I don't want you. I want Muncho!" I cried. I was also close to crying with my eyes.

"That stupid carrot is not here!" he growled, showing his true colours.

"Muncho is not stupid! Where is he?!"

I tried to slap him away, but he kept jumping around my shoulders with remarkable agility.

"Oh, didn't Muncho tell you?" he teased.

"Tell me what?" I was angry now, and horribly worried.

"You both wanted me here."

"No, we didn't!" I shouted.

"Yes, you did!"

"Go away!"

"I will leave whenever I want to leave," Rex sneered. "Muncho wished he had a companion, so here I am."

"Pray tell me when did Muncho make such a wish? I don't remember that."

"Why do you think he wanted to see Father Yuletide so much?"

"Oh boy!" Suddenly, all the puzzling puzzle pieces fell into place in my mind. That's what he'd been doing all those Yuletides in Caterham.

"Now what are we going to do about this little situation?" Rex asked.

"What situation?"

"You do not like it here, and no matter how many kites you fly, I know you miss home."

"This is home now."

"Is it?"

"I don't have a choice, do I?"

"Don't you?" he said. "Be a brat!" he cackled, like a wicked thing.

"It is not as difficult as you might think. There are so many ways to be a brat-"

"No!" Muncho appeared suddenly on my right shoulder, the hero of the hour. "Don't pay attention to Rex, he's the villain of this story!"

"Where have you been?" I cried out. I was so relieved. I had been beginning to feel the alluring lure of a life of delinquency and brattishness.

"I am here now! You will not be a brat or be naughty!"

I sighed a mighty sigh of moral clarity.

"Go away Rex," Muncho shouted. "Your advice is terrible and so is your face."

"Your face is orange!" shouted Rex.

"So is yours!" shouted Muncho.

"Actually my face is terracotta, because I'm made of lentils!" Rex yelled, but his face was getting slightly redder as he got crosser."

"Enough of all the yelling!" I yelled. "I have decided not to be a brat!"

From then on Muncho and Legumasaurus Rex were archnemeses. They would vy for influence over key decisions in my life, one pulling me in the right direction and one in the wrong direction.

9

ACCEPTED

The school was not as bad as I thought it would be, even now that I had Legumasaurus Rex to contend with. I was warmly welcomed by some Korean students who became my good friends. This made me long to see South Korea and try all kinds of food there, maybe videoing it for posterity. I grew to love living in Qingdao because of my Korean friends. When I first heard them speaking in Korean, I thought, "What?! There's another language that isn't German?!" Of course Rex tried to convince me that they were saying mean things about me in this new language, but a few minutes later I had the language nailed and was able to tell them all about my life in Catering as an astonishing child.

When I got home that day, I couldn't wait to tell my mother and father about what had happened.

"What happened in school today?" Mother asked.

"I met a friend. His name is Dongjun."

"Dongjun?"

"Well, he said I can call him by his English name, Andy. He is my new friend, and he is Korean. Koreans seem to be pretty cool."

It pleased my mother that I wasn't moping around mopily like a mopey moper anymore. My mother insisted we invited Andy and my other friends home on a weekend. Mother had gone overboard, making her famous banoffee pie and two dozen bakewell tarts. I was a bit nervous, which made me sweat tremendously. But who doesn't love banoffee pie? Only morons and Legumasurus Rex. Thus my friendships with my Korean friends grew stronger, and I yearned to know more about Korean culture.

We spent the holidays in Qingdao's glittering row of PC Bars, playing Starcraft until the early hours. We went to each other's houses, and I loved to try Korean foods. I wished I'd had a camera to make yummy noises into. Before long, I realised I wasn't missing England quite so much. Andy, his sister Rosemary and my other Korean friends, had welcomed me into their group and I felt completely at home in their company.

Going to university was not something I thought about much. School had been such a fun-loving environment that part of me didn't want to leave. I spent hours on my laptop, surfing the internet and looking at various schools and subjects. Muncho was there to comfort me, and he told me that eventually, I was going to discover what I was supposed to be, possibly in Chapter 23. He said I was probably already on an inevitable path towards it. I smiled, and ate some kimbab.

I first thought about studying German, but that subject was still too emotional and painful for me.

"What about mathematics?" Rex suggested.

I didn't even take the trouble to answer such a preposterous suggestion. Although mathematics is supposed to be a universal language, it was a language that just went over my head, into one ear and out of the other, and round the corner to the shop. Muncho and I had many lengthy discussions about what I should do and Rex had many unhelpful contributions too. One morning, I woke up and an idea sprung into my head like a springy little deer born among the daffodils just after the final frost of spring. There was something I loved doing, and that was speaking Koream and learning about Korea. I immediately turned on my laptop and looked for a university where I could study the Korean language. That was how I got to know about the School of Oriental and African Studies (SOAS) in London. I remember whooping at the top of my baritone voice, (I was by now one of the lesser known baritones in Asia). I first confided in Jordan. I wanted his brotherly advice.

"Jordan, I think I may have found what I was looking for."

"What's that?" he asked in a supportive fraternal voice.

"I want to study Korean language and culture!"

His mouth dropped open and his jaw hit the floor, then a second later it shot back up again.

"Having thought about it a lot," he said, "that makes total sense. Go for it." I felt so encouraged. However, when I told him I'd be moving back to the other side of the world he had to have a lie down. Upon rising, his emotions squashed back down, he gave me a hug, a salute and a secret handshake and said he would support me in following my dreams. As long as I believe, believe, believed in myself, he would believe in me too.

My parents weren't surprised either. I never knew they knew me so well but it turned out they did know me and knew that I knew that Korean was what I knew I wanted to know. I guess when you know you know, you know you know, you know? Korean language and culture were my passions, and I was determined to study them. I did not know what I was going to do with it afterwards but I knew that to study them was the next step on my path into the future present.

But first I had to be accepted. None of the other universities captured my imagination the way SOAS did. I summoned my courage and sent off my application. I drew little cartoon ramyeons on my form to give it an edge and to show that I really cared. Waiting was the hard part.

"These things take time, you've got to be patient," Father said. "A mighty oak tree grows out of the tiniest acorn."

I tried to be patient like an acorn. Muncho assured me that I was so good that SOAS couldn't possibly pass up the opportunity to have me as a student. I held on to those encouraging words of encouragement.

Jordan helped me to distract my thoughts by taking me to fly our kites together. Finally, on the first of August 2007, I got my acceptance letter from SOAS and so began the next chapter in the great adventure of my life, the details of which are in the next chapter.

10

Dinwiddy Towers

Getting into SOAS was a dream come true for me, just when I had lost all hope of getting in, mainly due to Legumasaurus Rex's attempts to tank my confidence. I had never been to London even though it was only three hours away from Caterham by horse, and there were excellent train links from Caterham Valley with a buffet service at weekends. I had heard so many interesting stories about London while growing up, and I longed to see the dreaming spires of La Sagrada Familia, bathe in the warm waters of the mediterranean as it lapped the shores of la Platja del Somorrostro, and browse the shops and tapas bars of Las Ramblas. Unfortunately all of these things were hundreds of miles away in Barcelona, so they would have to wait. Muncho was in awe at the sight of London, despite the thick smog, and I knew Rex was amazed too even though he tried to hide it.

"Look, London is nice and all, but you should have stayed in China. I prefer China!" Rex had said.

While I was in China, Rex had wanted me to get back to England and now that I was in London, he wanted me to go back to China. Rex was one confused bag of lentils.

"Oh, shut your cake-hole, Rex! London is beautiful. Josh, it's so beautiful!" Muncho chirped in delight, like a delighted chick.

"I told you," I said. "I heard so many stories about London while growing up, some of which weren't about Spain, and it feels great to finally be here!" I said, beaming.

"Yay! Yay! London!" Muncho yelled in excitement. "Can we go to the Plaza de Cataluña?"

"Sure, but first we must unpack."

My hall of residence, Dinwiddy Towers, looked exactly as it had in the brochure, except for the moving staircases and the ghosts, which were a surprise. My room was at the top of the tallest tower, and to get in you had to give the password to the lady at the bottom of the stairs. As I ascended the stairs for the first time a sadness sprung up inside me like a fresh water spring, (not a metal spring). I was going to miss home for the very first time. I was going to miss my parents, and I was going to miss Jordan like a beached whale misses the ocean.

Jordan acted like he didn't care that I was going to leave Qingdao.

"I will have the room all to myself and I won't have to listen to you talk to yourself all day, which can be so stressful," he said.

However, Jordan was quick to phone me soon after I arrived in London. I'd got lost in the prohibited forest and had to take a secret passageway back to my room to avoid missing his call. I told him all about my new surroundings, but he wasn't impressed,

"You have to share a room?" my little brother asked me, shocked.

"It is a student residence, Jordan; it's not a castle. In London there's not much space."

It took me about four days to really settle in my room, and another few to fully unpack. My valet, Blenkinsop, showed me how to settle my falcon in the falconry, how to launder in the laundry, and how to get food from the foodery.

I was eager to start classes immediately so I could meet people and make some life long friends. After my experience in Qingdao I wasn't afraid of not knowing anyone, but rather saw it as an opportunity.

On my second day in halls I finally got to meet my new roommate. His name was Dustin Dustin, and although his name sounded like the answer to the question 'what kind of cleaning are you doing? Answer me twice,' he was cool. I helped him settle into his half of the room, and explained the penalties for trespassing on my half. Dustin's parents wanted him to become a lawyer, and he was studying Aquatic Sciences and Knitwear, which meant we would both be in the Faculty of Languages and Cultures. Dustin Dustin was from New York, New York, and although he rarely spoke, when he did, he talked about America a lot. I understood a few things about the USA from watching TV and reading 'Where's Waldo', but I'd never dreamed of actually meeting a real American. Dustin seemed so exotic, and I was fascinated by the stories of his people. He told me how one of his parents worked in an oval office, and the other worked in a pentagon. Americans seem to really love oddly shaped working environments and that was fine by me. Dustin had never been to London before, and this was the first time he had left America. It made me feel more at home, because although I hadn't lived in London before either, compared to Dustin I was practically a native. I promised to show him all that British culture had to offer, and over the weeks and months that followed we became close friends, often meeting for a game of chess outside the Basilica of Santa Maria del Mar, before retiring to one of the many tabernas for tapas.

Anytime Dustin and I had intensive conversations about our cultures, Muncho and Rex came out to listen, and often Muncho would provide more insight on the topics, and make me look even smarter when I presented them to Dustin.

"You know your stuff, Josh," he would say. "You have experienced both the English and Chinese way of life. That's really cool. And you are going to experience Korean culture too when you get there to study. I think you should add America as your next stop after Korea. You would love it there. Promise me that one day you'll go on a big road trip across the states in a ridiculously short amount of time, and video it for some reason." I solemnly promised I would.

And so, as I lay in my little turret and gazed at the ceiling, things were looking up. I looked forward to a great year of learning more about Korea and meeting the people of SOAS. Classes started the following week, and little did I know that it would be a week that changed my life in the most wonderful way.

11

Meeting Ollie

My first lecture was on chimek, and how to review it on camera. At the time it seemed like an odd thing to learn, but the tutor assured us that it would come in useful one day, so I went along with it. As I looked at the delicious chicken, something seemed to resonate deep in my soul. It called to me somehow, like a hand from the future was reaching back into the present (which to the future was the past) and waving hello to my heartstrings.

On my first evening on campus I met another new student, who would change my life forever. Dustin and I were in the Great Hall, admiring the night sky through the invisible ceiling, and chatting to Mostly Decapitated Nigel, one of the ghosts. We were attending one of the banquets for new students, and just as the ninth course (swan flambe with asparagus jus) was being cleared away and the sifting hat was being removed for copyright reasons, a quiet descended. I looked around, and saw a student I hadn't seen before dressed in nothing but a cravat and pages from Dickens, stapled loosley to his torso. Apparently he had misunderstood the meaning of white tie and tales. I had no idea who he was, but could this really be the Ollie Kendal? I'd never heard the name before, but I knew I was in the presence of greatness. Just being near him was like watching the moon rise over the Taj Mahal while Beethoven played Shakespeare's sonnets and Elvis served drinks. I had never experienced love at first sight, but I knew this was no ordinary handsome, charismatic, debonair, urbane and devilishly talented man.

Words can't describe how I felt at that moment, but all at once I knew how Stanley felt when he found Livingstone; how Hannibal felt when he crested the Alps and saw Carthage; how Maureen felt when she first saw Daryl.

I was really hungry, but I didn't even notice. This was bigger than vol au vents; bigger than mini sausage roll; bigger even than Carrott sticks dipped in hummus (which my grandfather invented). This was huge. This was massive. This was really very big. It was so big that my mind couldn't comprehend its enormitude and from some angles it started to look medium sized. Then it dawned on me, like the sun rising over the Burning Swan memorial playground and casino in Caterham town centre. It was its comparative lack of size that made it truly gigantic.

We looked at each other. A pregnant pause gave birth to a moment that felt like an eternity as I waited, the placenta of my old life lying in the afterbirth of the new. Nervously, I spoke.

"Hi. I'm Josh."

"I'm Ollie and this is jolly. Listen, I don't have any friends. Will you be my friend?"

"Alright," I said, elated.

Ollie and I share a bromantic moment in Dinwiddy Towers.

Thus it was that our perfect union was born. I offered to seal it with a handshake but Ollie declined, thoughtfully warning me that his hands got sweaty when he was nervous.

Ollie had lived his whole life in London so he knew it back to front, but he always carried a mirror so he could see things from other peoples' perspective. He had been accepted to study on the condition that he tone down his brilliance so the other students didn't feel inadequate, which he was incredibly good at. He never said, but I assume they'd made the same demand about his appearance. I was overawed by Ollie from the moment I met him, and it was obvious that most other students felt the same, because when I was with him people generally kept their distance. Ollie had this amazing way of making you feel like he was the most interesting person in the room, without ever feeling the need to actually say anything clever or interesting.

Ollie and I became closer as the term progressed. We hung out pretty much all the time, which I was aware of because there were so many sundials in London. He was always over at my room, and I was always over at his. It was really annoying because we wanted to hang out in the same room. One day we decided to start arranging where to meet, which meant we could spend a lot more time together. He became my best friend, almost like a first wife, and our friendship became stronger as the weeks turned to months, and the months turned to clichés.

Like everyone I've met, Muncho loved Ollie, and it always excited him when Ollie visited us. Muncho was sad again because Ollie couldn't see him. I wished Ollie could see him, because I knew he would love Muncho as much as I did, if only he could see him, which he couldn't. Legumasaurus Rex, too, was fond of Ollie although he tried hard to hide it. Ollie made him laugh so much and, when Ollie was around, Rex had less time to be nasty. He was almost pleasant sometimes.

Ollie and Dustin became friends too, and the three of us would hang out in my room in our free time. Dustin always talked about how demanding his underwater crochet classes were, and at one point he had thought about switching to something less stressful like medicine, but in the end he decided to stick it out.

Over the first term Ollie and I were becoming inseparable, especially after his accident in adhesive class. Our friends jokingly referred to us as a couple because of how close we were. We were like a less handsome version of Shandy. We were always together, and it was in those early days that I really got to see Ollie's mischievous side. Ollie did a lot of crazy things in school, like attending some of my classes for the fun of it. Sometimes I attended some of his classes for the fun of it. It was really annoying, because we wanted to hang out in the same classes, but we worked it out eventually. Muncho loved attending classes with me. He loved to learn new things, and he loved meeting new people, even though they couldn't see or hear him.

12

Studying Abroad

Because I was studying Korean language and culture, and there's very little of either in London, I had the chance to move to Korea for a year to continue my studies. I was excited to see the country and meet more Korean people, who had always been so friendly to me in Qingdao, but I was sad to be leaving Ollie. Muncho was the most emotional of us all.

"Can't Ollie come with us to Korea?" he asked, little carrot juice tears rolling down his face.

"I wish he could, but he has to stay behind in London."

"But why?"

"He can't move with us to Korea because he would miss his classes here, and he would also miss Lizzie." Lizzie has asked not to be included in this book, but she is happy with this sentence clarifying that she exists, and this other sentence helpfully explaining the first.

Legumasaurus Rex was bothered too, but as always, he showed less emotion. When it's hard to say what we mean with words, it can be helpful to turn to meaningful art instead. Rex made a giant sculpture of a potato in honour of a year of happy memories (because Ollie's face had always reminded him of a potato). Obviously a potato is pretty easy to make into a sculpture, it's nowhere near as inspiring as other root vegetables, but it was still impressive in the circumstances. Being unable to see Rex, Ollie thought the sculpture was from me, and it didn't hit an emotional chord with him at all.

When I arrived in Korea that familiar feeling of loneliness crept over me again, as it had done on my first day of school. 'Hello darkness, my old friend' I thought, but stopped myself going any further for copyright reasons. The problem was I didn't know anyone in Korea, and I felt like hiding in my room and forgoing the sights and sounds of Korea that I had dreamed of for so long. But then I picked myself up (I had the longest arms in the prefecture), gave myself a stern talking to and I knew what I must do to avoid feeling so low. In order to seek my soul's solace, I sought to see Seoul solo. So I did.

I called Andy, my best Korean friend from school in Qingdao. He wasn't in Seoul as he was also studying abroad, but he was super excited for me. We talked a lot about the richness of Korean culture, and he was impressed to see that I had made so much progress since high school. He suggested some places he thought I should visit and foods he thought I would love. He said he had plans to return to Korea when he completed his studies abroad. I took Andy's recommendations and slowly I came out of my shell, like an agoraphobic oyster. I realised Korea really was everything I had imagined and hoped for, and for the second time in my life, I was in love.."Don't you miss Ollie? Because I do," Muncho asked, licking creme fraiche off his leaves (hedgehogs were a problem here too, and our room had just been fumigated). Muncho was always excited when I talked with Ollie over Skype, and he loved our long and goofing conversations. Ollie told me stories about what was going on back in SOAS, and I told him stories about Korea and all the wonderful people I had met. One day Ollie announced that he was planning to visit me in Korea!

"You cannot be serious," I said, Muncho doing cartwheels of joy behind me.

"I am. You have said so much about Korea, I've been dreaming about it. I want to float down the mighty Zambezi in a whale bone canoe, and witness the migration of the majestic mongoose, as sure as Kilimanjaro rises like Olympus above the Serengeti."

"So do I, but that's six thousand miles away in Tanzania. How about the Namsan Tower and some kimchi?"

"Alright then."

A few weeks later Ollie arrived, with our friends Kit and Ben. Muncho gave me the itinerary he'd carefully prepared and pleaded with me not to mess it up. Having Ollie, Ben, and Kit - two people I liked very much and Ollie, who I loved - in Korea for their first time was so exciting. Just like a year earlier with Dustin Dustin, I felt like a local showing off my adopted homeland.

We could not pass on the Seoul Tower. The tower sits 600 metres up, almost on top of a mountain, and although the climb nearly killed us it was worth it for the incredible views of the city below. From up here the people looked like tiny people and the ants were completely invisible.

I wanted to show the guys everything in Seoul, so we packed a lot into their trip. We spent hours on Hangang Park, belted out royalty-free classics at the norebang and tried different dishes for every meal. I was delighted and slightly confused to discover that Ollie had fallen in love with a street toast stall in Yongsan called 'Isaac's Toast', an obsession that continues to this day. It was really satisfying for me to see them enjoy the wonders Korea had to offer and I hoped this was something I could continue in my future life. On their last day in Seoul we visited an art shop and Ollie would not shut up about purchasing a plaster cast bust.

"Why do you want a bust so badly?"

"It's beautiful! It would be nice to have it in my room in London."

And so began Ollie's long history of buying crap he didn't need. Of course he bought the bust, but it was too big to fit into the plane, so when we got to the airport he used his pen knife and cut off its head. He cradled the severed plaster noggin on his lap for the entire flight back to London.

Ollie preparing to board a plane in Incheon Airport with the pre-severed head of his beloved bust.

My friends only spent a week in Seoul, but it was clear what a big impression it had made on them. They were mesmerised by how beautiful and vibrant the culture was.

"It felt like we were in a completely different world. Coming here made us realise that there is so much out there that we are yet to discover if we dare to say yes to adventure and no to misadventure. Thank you Josh, for showing us such an incredible place," Ollie said, poetically.

"Yeah, it's good," said Kit, not very poetically.

"Yeah, nice," agreed Ben, equally unpoetically.

Ollie told me he missed me and he wished he could stay longer in Korea. Muncho wanted him to stay longer too. Legumasaurus Rex almost cried at the airport.

"Are you crying?"

"No..." he cried.

"It's okay if you cry, Rex. We all are going to miss Ollie and that's ok. You do not have to pretend that you don't care."

I was sad to see them go, but I knew that we were still BFFs, and in Ollie's case BWFs. Our apartment was quiet when we got back, the stillness making me reminisce on the fun we'd had. As much as I loved Korea, I was a little homesick and part of me wanted to be done with second year quickly so I could go back to London to see Ollie. The following weeks were intense. It involved a lot of assignments, studying and preparing for tests. I had my plate full, so I was not all that sad and lonely, or hungry. Ollie and I continued to have our weekly Skype calls, and we updated each other about what was going on in our lives. One day when I was feeling particularly homesick he sent me something which made me smile and cry at the same time. Ollie had made a video of all our friends dancing to 'Human' by the Killers, holding a sign with the words "I miss you Josh." I wept in gratitude for what an amazing friend he was. The video arrived at just the right time. Just when Muncho and I were incurably sad, the video cured our sadness. It was also the first video to feature many of the attractive faces which would become household names on Youtube channel a few years later: Johnny, Lizzie, Jenny, Shandy and composer Andy.

A still from Ollie's moving 2008 video, "I Miss You Josh"

13

HAPPY BIRTHDAY

Second year was over, and I headed home to Qingdao for the summer holidays. Muncho and Rex were so happy that they sang for a very long time on the plane. It was sweet at first, and then became kind of emotionally draining, but I didn't want to dampen their joy, so I let them sing for twelve hours non stop, even though the only song they knew was 'Happy Birthday'. My parents and Jordan were excited to see me. Jordan had grown taller and had turned into a fine gentleman. I was so proud of him that I sang 'Happy Birthday' to him. It wasn't his birthday, but I just couldn't think of any other song.

I had brought presents from Korea for my parents and brother. I knew my mother was going to love the face masks I got her. She always gushed each time she saw the flawless skin so many Koreans had, also she wanted to occasionally disguise herself.

I brought a lot of Korean snacks, which Jordan and I enjoyed while watching 'Pride and Prejudice with Zombies', a film that always reminds me of home. I got my father some Korean tea, which he loved so much that he drank fifteen cups in a row before his usual fifteen evening coffees. It was nice spending time back in Qingdao with family and old friends. I caught up with Andy and discovered he had a girlfriend.

"How did you do it?" I asked earnestly.

"Well I was just kind, charming, nice and honest. I think girls like that," he shrugged.

"What?!" I asked, completely boggled. I was living in a mad world.

My room at home looked quite different. Jordan had migrated from his bed to mine, which was strange because I had written 'Josh' on it in semi-permanent marker. He had changed the wallpaper in the room to some music stars that I had never heard of. I don't like to talk about it, but I don't really like music, I prefer the sound of light machinery, except for the song 'Happy Birthday' of course, which everyone loves, even though it has complicated copyright issues. The changes didn't bother me. It made sense for Jordan to curate his safe haven of personal space into a space that he liked personally. But it did bother Muncho.

"I don't like change of any kind!" he cried.

"Change can be hard," I consoled him consolingly. "But if you don't let the river run you get sucked into a quagmire of facsimile."

I told my family about university life. Jordan loved to listen to my funny stories. I told them how I had met the remarkable Ollie Kendal for the very first time and how courageous he was to walk up to me. He wanted to know more about Ollie since I kept mentioning his name at home. My parents wanted to know more about Ollie too, and they eventually got to meet him during one of our video calls.

"He seems like an upstanding member of the community," Mother said.

I told them stories about Korea and the wonderful people I met. The video Ollie sent me made my mother tear up and put on a face mask as a disguise.

"That is so incredibly moving, what a guy," my mother whispered, overcome.

Ollie was back home with his family and I noticed that his father seemed like a proper English gentleman. I felt like I would like to give him many kinds of Korean food and hear his thoughts about them. In my mind's ear I heard him telling me those thoughts accompanied by a soundtrack of rousing royalty-free classical music. Ollie decided we were going to live together in our third year, so he searched for apartments while I was still in Qingdao. I looked forward to the end of the holiday so I could go back to London. Living with Ollie was going to be so much fun, we were going to make cheese sandwiches! Apparently, Ollie knows exactly how to cut cheese perfectly. Muncho and Rex were excited too.

14

PRANK WAR

I moved back to London to live with Ollie. It felt good to breathe the fresh smog of London, to crack out my party top hat and regrow my famous handlebar moustache. We stayed in a wooden hut near the whooping willow with our friends Kit and Julia. Muncho loves decorating, so he begged me to allow him to put his expertise to work. He had visions of magnolia wallpaper and chandeliers, but we wanted something a little more rustic, so we painted it silver and added many digital clocks. I planned to put these clocks away if Jordan ever came to visit, because of his fear of time, but Jordan, ever the hero of his story, told me that actually it was only grandfather clocks that gave him the heebeegeebees by then, which were much easier to avoid. What a relief! Finally, I could embrace my love of digital clocks! So I got ten more and glued them to the ceiling above my bed so that I could see them all as soon as I woke up and I could look at them with my open eye while my slow eye got ready to open a few minutes later.

Third year was our final year at university and we were determined to make the most out of it. I had a list of things I planned to do. I wanted to write 'buy more digital clocks' on it, but I was worried it was getting excessive, perhaps just one more. One thing I hoped might happen was meeting a girl. It would be great if I found one with her own opinions, that weren't necessarily the same as mine. Maybe that was crazy. In that time I only met girls who needed grandfather clocks in their lives, and that was never going to work out. Also, Legumasaurus Rex had advised me to call all girls 'baby' and to explain what they were trying to say while they were trying to say it, which turned out to be bad advice. It was even worse than Muncho's advice, which was to just go up to a girl and give her a puppy, which was just irresponsible. So instead of dating girls, I cemented my friendship with Ollie Kendal until it became solid like quick drying cement, like rock but man-made.

As it was our third year, the studying became more intense. We had to spend more time at home and ended up getting quite creative with our home-based shenanigans. We invented incredible games like 'who can get top of the stairs first'. Ollie always won that game, but that all changed when we brought in rules about not elbowing people viciously in the face.

We also played cards and I usually won because I had Muncho and Rex spying on the others' cards. It was easy! But, in some inexplicable way, it did take some of the joy out of winning. We played a lot of board games too. Kit was very good at board games like scrabble and chess, he had a thinky sort of mind, but I always won at monopoly because I had a win-y sort of mind and I'd been practicing since my third birthday.

Rex started a prank war with Ollie that I had no idea would take off. All he did was chop Ollie's special sandwich cheese in an irregular way and Ollie went ballistic. Next thing I knew, Ollie had changed the time on all of my digital clocks so that one alarm went off every five minutes of the day, instead of all at once when I wanted to enjoy the sound while waiting for my slow eye to open. It was sweet revenge indeed. Next Rex swapped the salt and the sugar so that Ollie put two dozen teaspoons of salt in his tea rather than two dozen teaspoons of sugar. It tasted much less sweet and Ollie was not happy. If there's anything you need to know about Englishmen, it is that tea is sacred and not to be messed with. It's how people know they're English. They drink tea and they go 'ah, yes, now all is well and I've got my bearings'. If you mess with their tea you're basically insulting their national identity and well as their sense of equilibrium. You just don't do it unless you want an almighty hullabaloo.

The prank war was actually a problematic time for me and my moral code. Legumasaurus Rex could not be reasoned with and I hadn't told Ollie about Rex or Muncho, so I had to take responsibility for everything they did. Generally Muncho's pranks were so small nobody realised it was a prank, like when he changed the way the loo rolls sat on the holder, who cares about that?! Or one time he pre-sauced Ollie's chips all over rather than having a sauce oasis at the side of the plate. I noticed, but the others just thought I was attempting to save on dipping time and congratulated me. It was all I could do to resist pointing out the occasional sauce drenched chip which was fully coated in ketchup, an absolute abomination to me. One time I came home and Ollie had wrapped everything in the house in tin foil. He thought it would be a hilarious prank, but I had to confess I loved it. It went really well with the silver walls and digital clocks and so I convinced the others to leave it that way. It did make it more time consuming when you were looking for a specific item and you had to unwrap and rewrap at least a hundred items each time, but it was so worth it. Everytime I looked around I felt inspired.

I walk into my tin foiled room.

The pranks got more intense and things escalated so that you couldn't approach a door without somebody having swapped it for a movie-set door and bursting through it. Ollie had bought a load of trick props, like glasses made of sugar. For months, every time I poured a drink my glass instantly dissolved. However, things did get confusing for me, especially as I could never think of any pranks myself and I had to take credit for all of Rex's pranks. Also, the only thing I was blamed for which I actually did wasn't even a prank. I had caught the scent of hedgehogs and I know from experience that hedgehogs have to be dealt with quickly or it gets out of hand, so naturally I filled the hut with creme fraiche. No one even said thank you. Fortunately all the foil made it really easy to clean up. The final straw in the saga was when Rex pooped on a plate and left it on my bed. He'd got overexcited and pranked me instead of Ollie!

"This is disgusting!" Julia exclaimed, turning to Ollie. Julia has thoughts and emotions. "Why would you do that?" she asked.

"I didn't!" Ollie protested. But nobody believed him.

"Oh man," Kit said. "You messed up big time bro. This is huge!" He meant both metaphorically and actually.

"Who else would have done it?" Julia demanded. Now was my time to speak up, but I couldn't. I have never had Jordan's courage to face up to things that I fear. I was afraid they would all think I was crazy, or a terrible liar, if I told them about Rex and Muncho. I felt I had no choice but to say nothing at all. Kit and Julia really let loose telling Ollie he was a cad, a wastrel and a scally goon. Ollie was crushed. I still feel pretty bad about it. I had let Ollie down, I'd let my parents down, I'd let the school down, and more importantly, I had let myself down. And even more importantly I'd let Ollie down.

15

Graduation

University is one of those once in a lifetime experiences that we can only experience once in our lifetime, unless we either don't go to university or we go back to university later in life. It was a stage in my life that came with so many blessings and so many different people. Third year was rounding up soon and exams were just around the corner. The day of graduation was coming so close and I became nostalgic. What would I do when we left and had to carve and forge our own way in the world?

Ollie was nostalgic too, and he had mixed feelings about graduation. Do not get me started on Muncho. Rex was also in a very positive place, he had finally found love in the form of a chickpea chinchilla called Squilla. Unfortunately she was someone's else's spirit guide's archnemesis, so they didn't get to see each other much. Who knew where the spirit guidee would end up. Rex was worried about this, but he was also living blissfully in the moment and seizing precious time with Squilla whenever he could. He was so mellow that it made Muncho nervous, which was unfamiliar to him. He even kept forgetting the words to 'Happy Birthday', his favourite song. You meet people at different stages in your life, some stay for a while and leave, some stay forever, some you get to see occasionally and others never, some you see more than you want to and some you see only in a metaphorical sense. Was I going to see Ollie again? In real life as well as in my mind life? That was a question I couldn't answer. I remembered the first day I met Ollie.

It all happened so fast and all I could think that day was: 'who is this boy and why is he so funny?'

Our graduation day finally arrived. My family had ridden their horses down from Qingdao the previous day to attend. It took place in a large hall where all the graduates stood for a long time in two columns with a large aisle in the middle. The atmosphere was overwhelmed with a thick smoke of relief as the Death Star had just been destroyed. I wore my shiny knee high boots and processed down the aisle to the sound of loud trumpet music. Nobody said anything. I looked at Ollie, Ollie looked at me, we both looked at the lady presiding over the ceremony. I smiled, she smiled, Ollie smiled, R2D2 beeped and Chewie groaned. She put gold medals on our necks and everyone clapped. It was so moving. And that was that. We were officially grown ups.

16

Dauxcited

Finishing university is a tricky point in the life of a young Carrott, because although I had been unanimously voted the friendliest graduate in SOAS history, I didn't really know what I wanted to do next. I would lie in bed at night, my mind awhirl with the big questions of life. Did my future lie in England, China or Korea? Could I bear to be apart from Ollie again? Do bald people get dandruff? How do you know you know, you know? Are we human or are we dancer? What's love got to do with it? Should I stay or should I go? The clash of options clanged around my head like a massively symbolic cymbal, and my mind was full of questions and copyright issues.

I always say life is a journey and we must pass through life's phases till the day we leave earth. I don't believe this at all, but I always say it anyway. The good thing about being a student is that there is a routine laid down for you. You go to classes, study, meet friends, play aerial broomstick games and steal social media platform ideas from your friends. But everything changes the moment you graduate, and you wake up on a Monday morning with no idea what to do or how to fill the time on all your digital clocks. It suddenly hits you that in three years of world class education you never learned how to whittle. You can still only disco dance at an intermediate level. You still don't really know whether eyebrows count as facial hair. It's a lonely time too, even with imaginary vegetable pals to keep you company. All your friends have gone back to their cities or countries, and you're not sure when, or even if, you'll see them again.

To cope with missing Ollie, Muncho had taken an interest in classic Russian literature, and most evenings he would force Rex and I to listen to great passages from his vegetable versions of Dostoyevsky and Tolstoy. This helped distract Rex, who was pining for Squilla, his chickpea chiquita, as she was at sea. In fairness to Muncho, War and Peas still worked despite the action being moved from nineteenth century Moscow to a kitchen garden in Basingstoke, but Crime and Punishlentils seemed to revolve more around the trial and imprisonment of a certain bean-based dinosaur than Rex was comfortable with.

After several weeks of apathy and boredom, I prepared my CV and sent out some job applications. I'd had a few offers from family members. My mother's brother, Uncle Gibbous, owned a toffee factory, but it didn't feel like something I could really get stuck into. Likewise my Aunt June's waterslide company just felt like a slippery slope towards a pool of boredom. After two weeks of sending out my CV, Ollie called and said that he was now working with a homelessness charity. I told him I was still sending out applications, and he told me not to worry, that a job was right around the corner. I hoped not. Right around the corner was Auntie Oona's road sign company and all I could see there were dead ends.

And so it was that I found myself working as what the French would call 'an administrator at a language school in central London', if they were speaking English. It was not what I had imagined myself doing, but it was slightly better than staying in my apartment braiding my eyebrows. I was basically helping students to access the right departments, wording documents for distribution and showing people where to find the powerpoints. It was hardly fulfilling, but the speed with which I started to excel did improve my outlook. I always say that the hardest thing in the world is a diamond.

After a while I got promoted to salesperson. Was it a blessing? I couldn't say, but what came with being a travelling salesperson was the freedom to leave my desk and go out into the field. I never thought in all my years that I was going to sell language training in a field, but there I was. Eventually, I decided to try it in a town, and things started to take off. It's like I always say, cows aren't interested in furthering their careers through the attainment of language skills. They literally only care about grass.

All the while I missed Korea. I pined to go back to the country of so many happy memories and mouth-watering feasts. I also missed Ollie and all the adventures we'd had together. We were both so busy at work that we didn't get to spend much time with each other. He couldn't find the time to come over to my place, and I couldn't find the time to go over to his. We couldn't even find time to meet in the middle, which we'd got the hang of by now. That was the harsh reality of our lives. Time, once enemy to Jordan and then friend to me, no longer favours you when you grow older. Eventually time moves so fast that no amount of digital clocks can help you keep up, unless every sixty seconds you set each one forward by a minute. Then you should be ok. Time wasn't anything pivotal when I was much younger, I have barely any memories of it at all except when Mother would put it in soup. I do remember one time, when I was eleven, I woke up just before I normally do and was slightly surprised. It's not my best story, but I think it helps to illustrate whatever point I'm making.

Ollie and I called each other on the phone whenever we had time (which was rare) and he liked to update me on his developing video-making skills. I longed to be back in our student house passing freely available time making silly videos. I went back and watched some of the old classics like the toboggan stair race and potato launcher series, and Muncho gushed over his filmmaking and editing skills. Rex, who had developed a pretentious interest in classic movies, did what he loved to do best.

"There are a few errors here and there. It's easy to tell that it wasn't made by a professional," said Rex, turning back to watch All Quinoa on the Western Front. "Ollie's trying hard, but visually it's no Citizen Kale."

In the summer of 2013, Muncho had the most ridiculous idea ever, or so I thought. I'd come home from a tiring day in the field selling Gaelic classes to sheep, and I fell asleep on the sofa as soon as I lay down. Just as I was dreaming about being in Korea with Ollie, having fun and going to different places, I heard a loud voice whisper my name. And then a smack on my forehead. My right eye flew open, and Muncho was on my chest, a wide smile on his face.

"I have an idea!" Muncho screamed, a little unhinged. "You and Ollie should start a YouTube channel!"

"Muncho, have you been at the beetroot juice again? What am I supposed to do on YouTube? Makeup tutorials? I'm good, but I'm not that good."

"Hear me out, Josh!" he cried. "Remember all those funny videos you and Ollie filmed while in school? The totally brilliant ones that everyone loved? Why not make videos about Korea and introduce it to your friends in London? With your language skills, Ollie's extraordinary editing prowess, the your bromantic love of a thousand best friendships, I bet you could get tens of followers!"

Muncho was right. It was a brilliant idea. I called Ollie later in the day when I got a bit of precious time and told him about it. Whilst the idea was exciting, the prospect of starting a YouTube channel was also a little frightening. What if it was a disaster, and people found it boring? We had shared our videos before but only amongst our friends, who were always completely positive about them. Creating a video and posting it on the internet so tens of people could watch it took guts. But even at this early stage we instinctively knew there was a certain safety in our partnership. We knew we made a great team, so in the face of it all we were daunted, but excited. Dauxcited.

17

STARTING YOUTUBE

One of the first questions we had was what on earth to call our new project?

"How about Ollie Kendal and Friends?" suggested Ollie. "It has a nice ring to it." We all looked at him. "Ollie Baba's Magical Cave of Treasures?"

"You're an idiot," I said, for the first time. "How about a combination of our names?" I suggested. "How about Olsh?"

Rex snorted. "You might as well call it Jolly."

"It should be something succinct which really encapsulates who you are and what you do," Muncho suggested, thoughtfully. "How about... Once Upon a Time in Carrotland?"

"I don't mean to be rude Muncho, but that's a terrible title to give anything," I said. "How about Korean Englishman? Just 영국남자 in Hangul." We all agreed this was a brilliant name and now we were ready to actually make some videos.

We packed up Ollie's camera and microphone and headed out onto the streets of Camden, North London. The idea was to give Londoners some kimchi to try, while asking what they knew of Korean cuisine and culture. After a couple of hours we had a wide variety of responses, and after many hours of editing we had our first little five minute video baby. Now we just had to hope that people wanted to watch it. On the eleventh of August 2013, 1,490 years to the day since St John I began his reign as Pope, we blessed the internet with our first video.

For the first few hours we watched with our right eyes as the view count slowly ticked up. The only subscribers we had were the friends we'd told about the channel, but then something amazing happened. Unbeknownst to us, Andy, my best friend from school in Qingdao, had posted our video to a Korean website called 'Today Humor' and suddenly it was going viral. The view count started shooting up and so did our subscribers. Over the next few weeks we surpassed Muncho's wildest dreams and reached not tens, not even fifteens, but thousands of people. Then hundreds of thousands. It was unbelievable. We struggled at first to keep up with all the comments and the love from our viewers, as well as filming more videos and still working full time. Somehow our honest desire to share the love of Korea with the people of Britain and vice versa had hit a chord, and after a year we were both able to quit our jobs and do YouTube full time. It was a risk, but we knew it was a risk we had to take, and as I always say, the riskier the risk, the rewardier the reward.

I prepare to film our second ever Korean Englishman episode in Ollie's living room.

My parents weren't so sure quitting my administrative job in the field was the right thing to do.

"What if YouTube falls off a cliff tomorrow like a lemming? What are you going to do then?" my father asked.

"YouTube isn't going anywhere, Father. It's a billion dollar company with no passport," I said, trying to reassure myself as much as him. "Besides, lemmings don't actually fall off cliffs; that's a persistent and widely held misconception."

My parents weren't convinced, which was understandable. Some say this mischaracterisation of lemmings originated over 200 years ago. Even if they had understood, making money online was an alien concept to them, like extraterrestrials, which they'd never heard of. Luckily my parents have always been supportive of my crazy pipe dreams, ever since I dreamed of playing the bagpipes. For Ollie and me, it was a calculated risk. We knew we could make good content that resonated with people, so we decided to make videos for as long as people wanted to watch them, which was usually between five and fifteen minutes. Working full-time on YouTube wasn't as easy as we thought it would be. We'd assumed it would be a walk in the park, but it was more like a run in the Botanical Gardens. The first thing was making sure to keep up with our subscribers. As our views and subscribers grew, we had to re-strategize because we knew people wanted more. The videos had to be well edited and of a higher quality than when we first started, but luckily one of Ollie's greatest qualities is a maddening devotion to perfection, so each video was more dazzlingly wonderful than the last.

In 2014, a year after we'd started our channel, something amazing happened. Jordan conquered his fear of calendars. Then Ollie and I got invited to a Korean culture convention, or K-Con, in Los Angeles, or L-Ang. I'd wanted to visit the United States, or U-Stat, ever since I met my roommate Dustin Dustin in my first year at SOAS, and the invitation was a big step for us. Being able to quit our jobs was one thing, but we never thought that 'Korean Englishman' was going to buy us our first tickets to the U-Stat! Second or third, sure, but not first!

Fourth, possibly. Fifth? It was certainly plausible. But first? Get out of here. Muncho was over the top with excitement. He loved going on planes, he loved everything Korean and he especially loved boy bands. He carrotwheeled with excitement when he heard that we had been invited to interview a new band called Bangtan Sonyeondan, or BTS. We had never heard of them, but we did a little research and thought about fun and important questions to ask them.

"Ask them where all the baby squirrels are," demanded Muncho.

"What on earth do you mean?"

"Have you ever seen a baby squirrel?"

"No…"

"Then I think it's time we got some answers."

Going to K-Con was a big step for us as a channel, but on a personal level it would turn out to be much bigger than I could have imagined. Huge in fact. Really mind-bogglingly enormous. Actually quite staggeringly - well, you get the idea. I couldn't know it, but it would be where I met the second love of my life.

18

Have You Ever Seen A Baby Squirrel?

We started our YouTube channel at a point in our lives where we felt a little stifled. It seemed like we had a volcano of creativity in our hearts ready to erupt, or a twinkling star of inspiration about to supernova out of our brains. It was intense, giving creative-birth to our futures. But, once we'd started, it felt like we had wind in our sails and tea in our teapots. It was exhilarating but also hard work and the invitation to K-Con was a welcome break from our new routine. We spent the next few weeks preparing for the trip to LA. Ollie dyed his eyebrows blue for the occasion and then changed his mind, what a fiasco. That took up a whole week's emotional energy. I enrolled in an emergency performers class. I thought it was a class for people who had been told they would be interviewing celebrities at short notice and I wanted to get a little confidence boost, but it turned out to be class for people who wanted to act as characters in the emergency services on TV shows. Muncho thought I should just leave, but in the end it was quite a moving experience. I spent five days pretending to be a firefighter and afterwards I really felt like I could connect with my father about it all. Now we had a wealth of common experience, mine emotionally real, his really real. Muncho prepared by working on a vegetable version of 'Anna Karenina' but he was too stressed out and ended up putting his 'And-a-cucumber' straight in the bin. Legumasaurus Rex was no use to anyone as he was desperately missing his chickpea chinchilla girlfriend Squilla. To make matters worse, while we were packing for the trip, Rex read that hummus comes from chickpeas, and had to lie down. The final thing Ollie and I did to prepare was to learn the BTS dance moves, in case we were asked to join in. If I'm being honest (which I always am because of my strict code of integrity) I have to say, Ollie is the most incredible dancer in the entire world. His moves are majestic. Wow. That's all I can say.

The journey to Los Angeles was a smooth one. Muncho and Legumasaurus Rex sang a little bit but then fortunately fell asleep after about an hour. We stayed at the USC hotel, which was a mere few minutes' journey from the Los Angeles memorial sports arena where the convention took place. All you had to do was to hop into a barrel and float down the aqueduct. Both Muncho and Rex would not stop gushing about how nice the hotel was and before I could stop them they had drunk all of the complimentary tea in the room. Ollie was furious. He completely lost his bearings. Also, he thought I had drunk all the tea, which made me look pretty bad.

"Sorry buddy, I was just suddenly really thirsty," I said feebly, my code in tatters. The serenity was peaceful, and the staff were so nice to us. They even put on bowler hats and cobbled the corridors to make us feel at home. That helped Ollie get his bearings back. That night we were too excited to sleep. I sang 'Happy Birthday' to Ollie to help him calm down but it didn't help. Then I pretended to rescue him from a burning building, which I was really good at now, but he said that put him on edge. I got no thanks. Muncho wanted to read to him but again I reminded him that Ollie would not be able to hear and that I wasn't ready to tell him about Muncho. It was a shame though because Muncho had moved onto Jane Austen for source material and 'Pride and Radishes' had turned out pretty good. The same cannot be said for 'Sense and Scents-of-broccoli' which was far too salacious. In the end I put on some soothing light machinery sounds and we drifted peacefully off to sleep. Fortunately, I'd packed a few dozen digital alarm clocks so we didn't oversleep. We were going to interview BTS and we needed to practice. Ollie acted as BTS and I interviewed him. After an hour or so, when my slow eye had finally opened, I suggested we try it without dancing, just in case.

The convention lasted for two nights and the turnout was massive, meaning that there were a lot of people. Fans were screaming and having the time of their lives. In that moment, I missed my brother-buddy Jordan. We had had the time of our lives so many times and it seemed to me that if he were here, this would be another time of our lives. The convention had a glorious array of Korean food, fashion, and music on display. It felt like we were back in Korea. My mind was blown every time I turned my head. I had to take a paracetamol.

The next day was just as mind blowing as the first, so I wore a neck brace to be safe. Since we had been invited to K-Con, we were given backstage passes, which was totally the coolest thing in the world.

We went backstage, almost expecting someone to say, "How did you crazy cats get those passes?" But, in actual fact, they said, "Can I see your passes?" and that was all! We were thrilled by the unfettered access these precious passes provided us, but were conscious that we needed to appear professional, so we put on our top hats and looked aloof.

Ollie and me trying on new top hats. Ollie is struggling due to his enormous head.

Interviewing BTS at K-Con in LA, 2014.

Eventually we got to meet BTS. I couldn't believe it! BTS was a boy band of seven extraordinarily talented members, Jin, Suga, J-Hope, RM, Jimin, V, and Jungkook. They were all really friendly and kind and all of their songs were just as good as 'Happy Birthday', maybe even better! The interview ended up going really well, I kept my cool and really enjoyed it. The boys were as friendly and talented as you'd expect and I was relieved we'd decided not to dance in front of them. In hindsight, Ollie definitely should have filmed the whole thing, but some reason he just got a bunch of random unusable footage from backstage. In any case, it went so well I felt like I might be okay doing more interviews in the future. Perhaps we could make celebrity interviews an unlikely centrepiece of our future YouTube work? BTS were one of the groups performing in the concert later in the evening and we were so pumped to go. Their performance was mind blowing. Fortunately, I had put my neck brace back on.

19

GABIE

The convention made me realise how much I had missed Korea and how earnestly I longed with all my heart to go back. Korea felt homely to me, like a home, and I felt welcome there. Ollie had had a great time too. Who wouldn't? But it was also kind of hard for him that he didn't speak much Korean and I had a degree in Korean and a natural penchant for languages and a better hair style, and a smaller head. I tried to be sensitive to this, and sang him 'Happy Birthday'. Unfortunately, loads of people joined in and it became a medium sized debacle. Our managers Katherine and Kate panicked and bought Ollie a cake and paraded it in with candles, while Ollie protested that it wasn't actually his birthday. There was so much incredible food to eat and so I went to see what I could find. Then something happened. Something so totally amazing that my neck brace came bursting off and shattered into a million pieces, because my mind was blown, big time. I met Gabie.

Sometimes, things just fall into place. If anyone had told me I was going to find true love at K-con, I would not have believed it. I had entirely given up on love and was satisfied with the companionship Ollie and Muncho gave me.

I first saw her across the room. She was wearing a chef's outfit and deeply engrossed in her work. She was putting the finishing touches to a giant swan made out of chimaek and glazing it with a fiery hot sauce. It reminded me of my parents' love story, involving a crispy swan, and seemed like a sign. She turned around and caught my gaze. It probably sounds like one of those love scenes in a movie, that I don't believe in, but it happened in real life for real.

She smiled and I said, "What an incredible swan made of fried chicken!"

"Thanks," she said. Her voice was like the music of the birds returning in the springtime and frolicking in the apple blossom. I had totally appreciated her for her skills and artistry and I could tell she liked that. I'm betting she also liked my top hat. Legumasaurus Rex yelled at me to blow her kisses and Muncho demanded I give her a puppy immediately, but I ignored them.

"Did you make all of this?" I asked, gesturing to the massive array of food and using exactly the correct amount of eye contact. Not so little that I seemed too aloof, but not so much that I seemed intense and creepy. I completely nailed it!

"I made these," she said, showing me a variety of delicious looking dishes that all looked delicious.

"Wowzers trousers," I said.

The exact moment I met Gabie for the first time, mixing 20 packets of Fire Noodles.

After that we got chatting and it was all very natural and true love-y. It was like the first shoot of a tomato plant breaking through the compost in a seedling tray: full of promise. We carried on chatting until she said she had to get back to work, but she gave me her number and I saved it in my phone as 'incredible fantastic brilliant Gabie'. Later, I texted her. It took me about half an hour to find her number as it was not under 'G' and I could have sworn I'd put 'amazing' in there.

It had been a whirlwind, but K-con was over and we were to leave LA the following day, never to return until we felt like returning. I missed Gabie instantly, and we texted, using words, emojis and the language of love. We had a lot in common. We had both lived in different countries. She had lived in Argentina, Spain, France and Korea and I had lived in England, China, and Korea. The conversation kept flowing and it felt like we had known each other for our whole lives, without knowing it. If you know what I mean then you know what I knew in that moment, when I knew there was more to know and that, in some way, I already knew it, you know?

20

Road Trippin' On Nothin' But Wendy's

After K-Con we embarked on an epic road trip across the Northern part of America known as the United States, or U-Stat for short. Our friends, Joel and Young, were in LA during that period and agreed to come with us to help with the driving and manage all of our top hats. The road trip was going to be very long, because it turned out that U-Stat is really quite big. We decorated our rental car beautifully with Korean flags and hit the open road. We had supplies, a car of some sort, and 6000km of exciting experiences ahead of us. Our plan was to drive from LA to New York (these are both cities in U-Stat) in ten days. I was glad to go on a road trip with the boys, but I was also so unbearably sad that I had had to leave Gabie and LA so soon. Already, I couldn't quite picture her face anymore, the memories were blurring, excepting the chimeck swan which was blazoned in my memory and I clung to it like Tarzan to a vine. I was preoccupied with the thought that I might never see Gabie again on this side of the grave. I really wanted to see her while we were both still alive! While the boys took turns driving and navigating, I eagerly texted Gabie about every 30 seconds.

"I thought you didn't believe in fairytale love stories," said Ollie,

"When have I ever said that?" I replied, askance.

"I dunno, like, the first line of Chapter 1?" Ollie was looking at me with wild eyes like a wild thing. I could tell he was bugged by my texting. He wanted me to turn keyboard clicks off but I just didn't have time to go through the rigmarole of it.

Ollie was in charge of accommodation and I was in charge of finding places to eat delicious meals. The following day, we got hungry, but I had been so preoccupied with texting Gabie that I had forgotten to search for a restaurant.

"Josh! We gave you one job! Just one job!" Ollie said, disgruntled.

We stopped at Wendy's and got Baconators™ and coffee. After dinner, we headed to our Airbnb, which Ollie had diligently organised while I had been texting, like Romeo. We were actually sponsored by Airbnb, which meant we got to stay in some amazing and some slightly unusual places. The first place Ollie had booked was perfectly lovely by daylight, but we arrived in the dead of night. A plethora of eery wind chimes directed us towards the door. As we crept forward, hoping it was the right house, we tripped over the carcass of a dead pigeon and screamed ourselves hoarse like we were being killed. It was a shock alright. Once we plucked up the courage to head inside we noticed a decorative skeleton on the wall and suddenly out of the darkness loomed a terrifying figure! It was man-ish and big-ish and sitting-in-a-chair-ish! But it turned out to be just an average mannequin sitting fully clothed in a believable position in a chair, absolutely nothing to be alarmed about!

In the morning we looked outside and realised that we had slept in an incredible house in the middle of the desert. It was the Joshua Tree National Park, which is a cool name. It kind of made it feel like I was meant to be there, like it was calling me, by my name. We set out into the Mojave Desert towards Las Vegas, where Ollie had again booked us an incredible place to stay with beds and a pool. We drove for hours. It was truly moving to look down at my phone and my messages as the glorious landscape and the sweeping skies sped past us. Suddenly I looked up and realised the sun had set spectacularly over the desert and the stars had come out and we were entering the bright lights of Las Vegas, which blocked out the stars. We were hungry and tired, and then it hit me, like a carrot cake to the face, that I had forgotten to find us somewhere pleasant to eat and the boys were furious with me. We had to go to Wendy's again. Not the same one, of course, but they are all pretty much the same except for location.

The next morning, I tried waking Joel and the others up. Joel is like the human equivalent of my left eye, he takes a while to wake up. He is like a caterpillar inside a cocoon, but if you give him the right amount of time, he will emerge like a butterfly ready to fly into opportunity. It was even harder to rouse Legumasaurus Rex, who just wanted to mope in bed. The previous night he'd just found out that falafel is made out of chickpeas and it really knocked him back.

We left Las Vegas and drove east racing to get to the Grand Canyon before sunset. I made a pact with myself to look at it with my eyes. We got there just as the sun started to set, and it was a truly moving experience. You absolutely, indisputably, completely and indubitably must go to see the Grand Canyon while you are this side of the grave.

Packing up our car for the long drive across U-Stat.

Filming mid-roadtrip in Denver, Colorado.

As the days went by, there kept being mix ups with the timings and our meal planning and we ended up eating nothing but Wendy's for three days. It was horrifying. It was partly this Wendy's induced state of terror that led Ollie to make one of the few miscalculations of our long and perfect friendship. For some reason, he thought it was a good idea to buy a Carrot Cake in a South Dakota Walmart and get our friend Michael Wicker to sneak up on me and slam it in my face as a joke. Wicker had joined us in Denver and was always keen for a little prank. Unfortunately, Ollie did not know the carrot cake was old, stale, and rock hard, and the impact nearly broke my nose. I was angry with Ollie, but after a lengthy emotional chat at Wendy's we made up and had a long hug.

Next we made our way to the Niagara Falls, which is worth a visit on this side of the grave, before heading for New York City. Approaching New York City was bittersweet. We were excited about seeing the famous city, but we were sad to be at the end of what had been an unforgettable journey. I rang up Dustin Dustin and said, "Remember I promised you that one day I'd go on a big road trip across the states in a ridiculously short time and video it for some reason? Well, I'm about to tell you something that will blow your mind." Then I told him all about Wendy's and texting Gabie.

21

An Epic Proposal

I always say, the thing about all good things is that they must come to
an end. What I'd never realised before is that the other thing about all
good things is that they must come from a start. I pondered this as we
saddled our horses for the long ride home from New York. Travelling
across America had been all kinds of fun except the well organised
kind, and I was sad it was over, but on the other hand my relationship
with Gabie was taking off like a soufflé in a wind tunnel.

As we headed back to London, Gabie was on her way home to Korea,
and I wasn't sure how I would cope being even further away from her.
It sounds ridiculous to pine for someone when you've only met them
once, but the closest I'd been to her was about a foot away, and we were
about to be several million feet apart. There's something about being on
different continents that just feels distant somehow. But, as I looked at
the sunrise each day, it was comforting to know that she was looking at
the very same sunrise, except several hours earlier. All I had to get me
through this tricky period was my unwavering belief in fairy tales and
romance movies, and my hope that our auspicious meeting would work
out as well for us as it had for my parents. As my father always says,
couples who witness a burning swan together, stay together. I knew in
my heart of hearts, and my brain of brains, and even my foot of foots,
that Gabie and I were destined to be together. She was the Romeo to
my Juliet, the Han Solo to my Chewbacca, the peanut butter to my jam,
spam and clams. Gabie and I had started texting each other more often,

and our conversations moved from superficial chit-chat to more serious life topics, like whether free will exists, and why you never see a baby squirrel. BTS hadn't shed any light on that subject. There was so much I admired about Gabie, from her polymathic command of languages, to the fact that she was so certain of her destiny in life. While I had been wondering what to do after university, Gabie had already known, with the clarity of a high resolution photo, that she wanted to be a cook. I also liked that we had so much in common, from our mutual love of cricket (the insect, not the game) to our mutual hatred of words that rhyme with types of cheese. That, I realised, was why we both loved souffle so much, it doesn't rhyme with anything. Except bouffle. (It was also why we both hated my neighbour Mrs Glubble-Doster so much). As time passed on my digital clocks and Gabie and I became closer emotionally, if not geographically, Ollie and I started to travel to Korea more often, so Gabie and I were often closer geographically as well as emotionally, but then further apart again geographically, if not emotionally, when we went home again. I was never particularly good at geography, which made the whole thing pretty hard to deal with. Ollie and Gabie got on like a swan on fire, making each other laugh and cry (with laughter) and this confirmed what I had known from the moment I first spied Gabie across that room at K-Con; that Ollie was a brilliant guy. And also, this was the girl I wanted to marry (Gabie, not Ollie). This was hard for me to comprehend, because I'd always thought of myself as a happy-go-lucky bachelor, more at home with a digital clock and an imaginary carrot friend, than a wife, but I guess now I knew what I'd known I knew before I knew I knew it, you know? The thing I'd known I knew was that I knew Gabie was the love of my life, and nothing Rex could say would change my mind. Muncho was happy for me of course, he loved Gabie almost as much as he loved Ollie, and he hoped that true love would enable her to see him. It didn't, and that was a shame.

I tried to make sure I spent time with Ollie, Muncho and Rex in between texting and calling Gabie, but my heart and mind were often elsewhere. Even my games of chess with Muncho no longer captivated me as they once had. A few years ago Muncho had invented his own version of chess where all the pieces were different root vegetables and his favourite opening was the onion ring's gambit. With all the different rules and roots, it was shallot to concentrate on. He'd recently tried to 'improve' other games, and insisted on hour long games of Monopoleek whenever I got off the phone to Gabie. Rex was even more grumpy and pretentious than usual, and his annoying habit du jour was dropping French words into sentences when there was absolutely no need. It was so passé, just like the time he pretended to be interested in fine wine, and went around telling everyone about his collection of bon vins. It was like deja vu all over again. It was tres tres exhausting trying to keep everyone happy, and I decided the best solution was for Gabie and I to be close both emotionally and geographically at last. It was time to marry Gabie and live happily ever after in London.

In 2015, just over a year after I met Gabie, I decided it was the right time to propose. I knew from all the wonderful and accurate romance movies I'd seen that I would have to do something big and dramatic. Gabie's sister Esther was living in Australia at the time and Gabie told me about her plans to visit her the next month. This was the chance I'd been waiting for. I chartered a horse bound for Sydney and told Esther my plan. I really wanted to propose on the beach, and I had an idea to surprise Gabie as she stepped from the Sugar Loaf Mountain cable car onto the warm sands at Copacabana. Unfortunately, as Esther pointed out, these things were eight thousand miles away in Rio De Janeiro, so she suggested a spot along the coast just outside Sydney. I agreed and the stage was set for the biggest moment of my life. As I boarded the first horse on my 27-hour journey I was so dauxcited that I weed a little. I decided to record the whole journey for posterity, and accidently made the most romantic video ever produced.

The date I'd chosen was Gabie's birthday, which added another dimension of magic to the brilliant plan. As I set up the cameras at the interception point and waited for Gabie and Esther to arrive, I contemplated the future I'd chosen. What if she said no? What if she said she didn't love me? What if she was already married? Whoever said a proposal was easy to do was lying, although now I think about it no-one has ever said that. As far as I was concerned, I hadn't been so sure of the rightness of something since the day Ollie and I had met and he'd asked me to platonically marry him in friendship. After 45 minutes Gabie arrived and I appeared as if by magic from behind a rock.

"AAAAAAAAHHHHH!" cried Gabie, romantically. She repeated this several times while I gave her the flowers and sang 'Happy Birthday' a few times over. Then I got down on one knee, and produced the ring. "AAAAAAAAHHHHH!" cried Gabie again, which I had come to realise was her way of saying: 'woohoo! My handsome and wonderful boyfriend is proposing to me! What larks!'

Eventually, Gabie managed an actual word, which was the one I was hoping for.

She said yes.

As we walked off together into the sunset, the planets rearranged themselves into a heart shape and the birds flew west for the spring. A gentle breeze played through the springtime apple blossom, just as it had when my parents met in Chapter 1. Remember that? Man, that was a good chapter.

Preparation for the wedding started immediately and, let me tell you, whoever said planning a wedding is easy was lying. Actually I've never heard anyone say that, but if anyone ever does, they're lying. There was so much to think about; we had to select a date that everyone could make, we had to think about the venue, the priest who was going to preside over the ceremony, what animal to have pulling the carriage, the food, the flowers, the dress, the decorations, the vol-au-vents, the cheese and pineapple on sticks, and so many other things. Accommodating everyone's lifelong fears took days, what a faff. It was hectic, but gradually things started to settle down. We decided on a date a few months away: the 11th of February 2016, 1060 years to the day since Tiberius Claudius Caesar Britannicus, heir to the Roman Emperorship, died under mysterious circumstances in Rome, and true love sure is mysterious too. As the best man ever, obviously Ollie would be my best man. We asked Ollie's brother-in-law, @RevChris7, to preside over the joyous occasion, because he was already a priest, which would save some time.

Marrying Gabie was the best decision I've ever made. Ollie was pretty excited too.

Gabie arrived at the wedding in a carriage pulled by horses. She looked so amazing in her dress that I wanted to marry her then and there. It was so lucky that that's what was happening. All our friends and future YouTube household names were there to wish us well: Crazy Johnny, Dan and Joel, Shandy, and composer Andy. @RevChris7 wore a GoPro and filmed the whole thing. At the reception Ollie gave the best best man speech I've ever heard, which was hilarious and touching in all the right ways. I've said it before and I'll say it again, what a guy that guy is. Muncho also gave an emotional speech that nobody else could hear, but he'd really put a lot of effort in and it nearly made me cry. After the meal Rev Chris taught us all how to dance and we boogied on down to Muncho's DJ mix. No-one seemed to notice the vegetable theme, and personally I preferred Muncho's version of 'We Are the Champignons' to the original.

At the end of the reception we said goodbye to our friends and family and got in the horse-drawn carriage to go home and start our new life together. I couldn't imagine being happier than I was right now. I mean right then. Then it was now, but now it's then.

22

JOLLY

At this point in my life, things seemed to be going swimmingly well. I was hitched to an incredible woman. 'Korean Englishman' was going down as well as a cobbled street and a top hat. The friendship between Ollie and I was so beautiful that it reminded me of the great Harry and Ron. I asked Gabie if she would like me to start calling her Hermione, and she said that 'Gabie' was fine for now, but that if she came up with a cool nickname she'd let me know ASAP. For a while, Ollie and I had talked about starting a new channel, with a bit more of a broader remit. We wanted to be a bit more experimental, and to try out experiments, without the pressure of it being on the 'Korean Englishman' channel, which now felt well established and we were naturally protective of it. We were like birds who had just learned to fly and were thinking about laying an egg, or squirrels who had been happily nesting in a roof and then felt like gnawing through a kitchen ceiling. Muncho was excited about a new channel and had come up with a good name for it, which he had repeatedly yelled in my ear at the wedding while I was trying to do my speech. It had been pretty distracting and I did worry that it affected my tone and made me sound less sincere, but you can't stop and talk to invisible carrots during a wedding speech. Ollie assured me I had sounded perfect, like the rustling of the breeze through apple blossom in springtime in Caterham. At the time I didn't know what Muncho was talking about. I just thought he was loudly expressing his emotions, and while I am all for expressing emotions, I had quite a lot on my plate that day.

"It's 'JOLLY'!" Muncho had shouted again and again. "It's 'JOLLY'!"

"Of course it is, it's a wedding!" I snapped when I finally got a moment. Muncho sang a few rounds of 'Happy Birthday', to calm down, and then explained that he meant that 'JOLLY' could be the name of our new Youtube channel.

"It is the combination of Josh and Ollie and it means happy!"

My mind was blown! Fortunately, I had anticipated emotion and had worn my neck brace for the wedding as a precaution. Thank goodness I had! I could have done myself a serious injury! I told Ollie and he went wild with glee. He had never had his bearings so completely as in that moment. He also thought I was a genius, which I had to take undue credit for of course, but it felt pretty good all the same. Legumasaurus Rex grumpily muttered something about him suggesting that name back in Chapter 17, we were all too excited to care.

We started making episodes and soon discovered that we had a sensation on our hands, a masterpiece that was born out of my perfect friendship with Ollie. It was also important that we maintained our friendship, as we would be appearing together on 'JOLLY' as friends, whereas in 'Korean Englishman' Ollie was only the videographer. It's like I always say, friendship is like a garden, plant carrots and you'll get carrots, plant potatoes and you'll get potatoes, plant erroneous information in a Wikipedia page and it'll eventually make it into a book, meaning said erroneous information on Wikipedia can now be cited, which is how rumours start. We uploaded our first video on 'JOLLY' on the 13th February 2016, the same date that Thomas Edison had observed Thermionic emission some many years earlier, and boy did we emit something great! We filmed it without having a concrete plan. In fact we hadn't really thought about concrete at all. We talked about what the channel was going to be about, even though we weren't quite sure. I think our charm and charisma were a big part of the appeal, so we dialed those up a notch. We had also really nailed the exactly right amount of eyebrow motion for emphasis, not so much that viewers got sea sick, but not so little that we looked like Legumasaurus Rex, who has no eyebrows and it's very disconcerting.

Ollie and me preparing to film our 1 million subscribers celebratory JOLLY episode.

We soon came up with a few ideas that seemed to work quite well. We did videos where I would attempt to teach Ollie Korean. He's an excellent student but could do with learning how to dress to impress and also just listening when I'm trying to explain something. Videos like this were also interesting to make because they didn't require as much planning and filming time as we usually spent on 'Korean Englishman' episodes. It freed us up to try different things and experiment experimentally and discover what worked. A lot of our videos involved trying different foods from around the world, in a similar way to what we had done with 'Korean Englishman'. We filmed a video where Gabie tried some of the UK's weirdest foods, like black pudding and haggis. She loved both of these, but then she tried jellied eel and threw up, instantly and understandably. This kind of video was great fun, but we also found that we could sometimes leave more space for our guests to talk about things a bit more deeply. For example, we made a lot of episodes with our friend Rev Chris, who is a real life priest, but is also married (which is allowed in the Church of England) to a genius writer called Jenny. Although 'JOLLY' is often rib-crackingly hilarious, it was interesting to have a space which could also deal with heavier topics and sometimes it made it feel more personally personal than we had personally expected.

I think there had always been a part of me that worried that the success of Korean Englishman had been a bit of a fluke, so it was gratifying to have started something new and distinct and see it strike a chord. We soon settled into the routine of video making, meeting our various upload deadlines on each channel, and enjoying the creative process. Of course, this meant that Ollie and I were hanging out more than ever, and the privilege of getting to work with my best friend was never lost on me.

I'm not able to read minds, but if I could have read Ollie's mind on those filming days I would have seen that he too was really grateful for my friendship and loyalty through it all.

Ollie's mind would have said, "Thanks for always sticking by me through the highs and the lows. You've consistently looked out for me, tolerating my weaknesses and selflessly championing my strengths. You know I wouldn't have got through the last few years without you, and I'm so grateful for your friendship in it all. I love you, man. P.S. Please forgive me for secretly writing and publishing your autobiography without your knowledge for a joke. I'm aware it's a bit weird."

23

A Prophecy In Carrotland

To our relief, the new channel was doing well, and that gave us warm fuzzy feelings. Warm fuzzy feelings are the only way to get through the winter in England. I always say, warm up and chill out, so about a year into starting 'JOLLY', Ollie, Lizzie, Gabie, and I (with Muncho and Legumasaurus Rex in tow) headed out to New Zealand for a much needed holiday. It was a place I had always wanted to go since reading 'Harry Potter' and I was really excited. We were also planning to film a few 'JOLLY' episodes while we were there, but little did we know, we would film not only the greatest 'JOLLY' episode of all time, but potentially the greatest YouTube video in the entire world, nay galaxy: 'Carrotland'.

In the foothills of Mount Ruapehu, lies the idyllic sun-lit town of Ohakune. On its Southern border lies Ohakune Carrot Adventure Park. It is an incredible place that reminds you simultaneously of all the stories you knew and loved from childhood and at the same time none of them. It is fresh and yet universal. It's most stunning feature is the world's largest fibreglass carrot figurine. It was one of the most beautiful things I've ever seen and so it made me think of Gabie. Apparently, Ohakune grows two-thirds of all the carrots in New Zealand and, as you travel through this eden of carrot-suited farmland, it is impossible to miss the roadside tribute to Ohakune's biggest crop. Standing a little over 7.3m tall, my smiling tasty-vegetable namesake has awed visitors since 1984 and is accompanied by a veritable salad bar of root vegetable artistry. There is a carrot themed car, see-saw and swings, which are far too small for adult-sized hips to fit in. We had a go on everything and talked about it all for a really long time so that we could crop it down into a snappy video. Not all of my speeches made the cut, for I made many. I was moved. I was stunned. I was affected by the effect of such a magical place. The place gave me fresh pride in being a Carrott and I longed to share the moment with my parents and my brother, my Carrott clan. For Muncho, this experience was a pilgrimage of self discovery after feeling uprooted and then returning to his roots.

As he sat on my shoulder weeping, he whispered, "Golly," and I knew he really meant: "We must come back here Josh, and make this hallowed ground, this sacred, orangey, vitamin A infused pasture, a centerpiece of our story. Who knows? Maybe one day, this very place will be the rousing crescendo of your bestselling autobiography!" I knew, in that moment, that Muncho was right.

After finishing filming, while Ollie went to use the convenient free-to-use porta-loos situated in the car park, Muncho and I were left alone with our thoughts. I had so many thoughts. I felt so many things. Muncho leant up against my cheek,

"I belong here," he said, wiping the tears from his face.

"I know. You're a carrot, I'm a Carrott, it's almost like a homecoming," I sniffed. "I feel like a bird returning to the apple blossom in Caterham after wintering in foreign and warmer climates. If only I had wings to swoop with. Boy! How I would swoop."

It was then that we heard a low hum humming. It was subtle at first, but grew steadily louder and more sonorous, until you could feel it in your bones. It was the sound of thousands of tiny feet, belonging to hundreds of imaginary carrots like Muncho, converging on their homeland. Muncho and I stood there transfixed, (I was 100% agog), as carrot after spirit carrot poured out of the neighbouring fields, woodland and sluice gates. As they gathered, they swayed and whooped in a trance-like state. Muncho suddenly hopped off my shoulder and joined the throng, he too in the throws of a hypnotic waltz. There were scores of carrots now, as far as the eye could see, imaginary carrots with arms and legs but no ears, swaying and swirling in unison, with me at their centre. It was a bit like the beginning of 'The Lion King' but with bequiffed vegetables. In disbelief I called out to Ollie, but my voice was drowned out by the cacophony of marching carrot feet.

As this orange kaleidoscope oscillated around me, I noticed a team of elite imaginary carrots clasp themselves together to form a human pyramid (except they were carrots not humans). About 300 or so wound themselves together, tighter and tighter, higher and higher, until they formed a teetering semi-solid mass before me. The emergence of this new pyramid and the endless sea of swirling orange behind it, temporarily disorientated me, my eyes unable to focus. I closed one eye, just to make sure I wasn't dreaming. Carrots covered the hills all the way to the horizon. They were dancing in the trees, dancing on the parked cars, even dancing on the portaloos. And then, in an instant, they were still. Total, silent, stillness. My eyes re-focused to see Muncho at my eyeline, hoisted on the carrot pyramid's apex, with his hand held high in the air. His signal had silenced the salady multitude. It was then, that Muncho spoke. The carrot congregation simultaneously mimicked his words in unison, amplifying his voice in a harmonious choral drone.

"Joshua Daryl Carrott,
our master, friend and root,
Thank goodness Ollie brought you here,
his brain is most astute.
So hear the carrot prophecy,
a-calling from afar,
to you adorned with extra "t",
our orange YouTube tsar!
A book as yet unwritten,
your story bold and true,
shelves stacked and readers smitten,
chart topping, plus a few.

> *And as the sales grow bigger,*
> *they'll raise a timely sum,*
> *to build this park a figure,*
> *for you, our carrot son.*
> *For this the place, but not the time,*
> *to reveal with great fanfare,*
> *a mighty statue most sublime,*
> *and meet your purpose there.*

Then Ollie returned from the toilet and all the imaginary carrots disappeared like wisps of smoke upon the wind in winter. All that was left of them was an 8 foot statue of Muncho in his silencing pose, at the centre of the park. I was still completely agog. But as I'm usually at least 80% agog, Ollie didn't notice. I was left to ponder what in the blazes it all meant. I had to ponder it in my brain, as none of it had been caught on camera and Ollie was attending to his irritable bowel syndrome in the free-to-use portaloos and so saw and heard none of it.

A few months later we released the 'Carrotland' episode, and even though it featured none of my carotenous prognostication, it still received almost universal acclaim, with every viewer agreeing it was a masterpiece. The vision that I had seen was perturbing, disconcerting, unsettling and discombobulating. To this day, I'm boggled, bamboozled and flabbergasted. But, I am eternally grateful to Ollie for insisting we stop at Carrotland. I hoped that one day I would know what it all meant, but I didn't know. Now I know, but you won't know until the next chapter, then you will know, or will you? No. I mean yes, you will know.

24

The Greatest Birthday Present

It was a normal filming day in late post-apple-blossom spring 2021. Ollie had prepared an episode to film but he had not told me anything about its content. He sat down in our 'JOLLY' studio, waiting patiently for my arrival, humming 'Happy Birthday' to himself. I stood outside the studio. For some indefinable reason, which I couldn't define, I didn't want to go in. The atmosphere had a completely different aura and I felt that, if I went into the studio, something crazy might happen. This was not an unusual feeling. In this series of 'JOLLY' we had filmed an episode where we reviewed Netflix's movie props and Ollie had replaced the studio door with an exact prop replica and burst through it when I wasn't expecting it. In another episode Ollie made me wear an electric facemask that gave me an electric shock every time I got a question wrong on an impossible quiz. Such high jinks were part and parcel of working with a genius like Ollie, but today I had reason to feel especially trepidatious; it was my birthday. Last year Ollie had surprised me with one of the greatest episodes since our Carrotland masterpiece from 2017: 'CARROTLAND: A CELEBRATION'. For lols I pretended not to enjoy either the original video or 'CARROTLAND: A CELEBRATION', but if I'm completely honest, they were both incredible pieces of work by a genius unrecognised in his time or neighbourhood. Being the best and friendliest best friend slash genius, I knew Ollie had something more than his Harry Styles tattoos up his sleeves. How, I wondered, could he possibly top 'CARROTLAND: A CELEBRATION'? Muncho encouraged me,

"Ollie is a good friend and an upstanding member of the community! Yes, over the years he has made you do some uncomfortable things. There was the time he ordered a whole canned chicken for $100 not including shipping, or when he slammed a carrot cake into your face in a Walmart in South Dakota... but all of those things, he did out of love. You can trust Ollie at all times. He is your best friend, and like a wife to you. Go in there and get your surprise gift – it is going to change your life!"

As it turned out, Muncho would prove correct - this surprise would change my life and my destiny, and fulfil the prophecy I had received in Chapter 23.

Filming started as normal, we did the intro and everything seemed to be going well, or so I thought. Ollie started by wishing me a happy 33rd birthday, which would have been nice if not for the fact I was turning 32.

"Oh-Oh. Ollie doesn't know your age," Rex said. "I smell trouble."

"SHHHH," Muncho said.

"I'm 32," I corrected him.

"I definitely said that on purpose," Ollie replied sincerely.

I could tell Ollie was nervous, and that made me nervous. He had a habit of hugely overdoing things in an entertaining and hilarious way. He said he wanted to do something extra special for my birthday this year. He described embarking on a project that was bigger than anything he'd ever undertaken before. A project so bigly big, it had involved hundreds, potentially thousands of hours of work, and dozens of people around the world. He then brought out a small brown package and handed it to me. I opened it slowly, my heart thumping heavily.

Reader, what I was holding in my hands is the very book you are reading. Ollie, like the amazing friend he is, had kindly written my autobiography. I was stunned. Only a week earlier while out on a walk, I had told him for my birthday I'd like a 'must-read book, preferably an autobiography, but nothing too heavy, maybe something funny?' And now this.

Stills from our greatest ever JOLLY episode, "Carrotland"

Ollie told me to turn to page 108 and read aloud, starting from the next sentence.

As I cradled this symbol of our eternal bond, I choked back a tear (imperceptibly), turned to him and said ecstatically, "This is the greatest gift of all time. Kabooya, kabooya, I say again, but with more gusto, KABOOYA!"

My mind was racing, like a carrot racing-car, and yet there was a pregnant pause. I could see on Ollie's face there was something he was holding back. He was literally holding something behind his back.

An orange envelope, which he gave to me, saying, "Josh. The book was only the first half of your birthday present. Open this so the prophecy can be fulfilled."

I opened it and read it aloud:

> Dear Josh,
>
> On behalf of the Ohakune Carrot Adventure Park Trust, I would like to congratulate you on the publication of your autobiography. I would also like to express our gratitude to you for committing to funding a new statue in Ohakune Carrot Adventure Park from the proceeds of the book. Naturally the statue will be in your honour, and once funds have been raised we can work together on a fun design. I have been in contact with Ollie, and he is confident that your fans, the 'Jollybeans', will buy enough copies to make this dream a reality! I hope to welcome you back to the park in due course for a grand unveiling.
>
> Best wishes and happy birthday!
>
> Dave Scott
>
> *Founder and Custodian*
>
> *Ohakune Carrot Adventure Park (Carrotland)*

Ollie told me the book was launching a few days later and our fundraising for the carrotland statue would commence in earnest.

OHAKUNE CARROT ADVENTURE PARK
TRUST INC est 2018

Dear Josh

On behalf of the Ohakune Carrot Adventure Park Trust I would like to congratulate you on the publication of your autobiography. I would also like to express our gratitude to you for committing to funding a new statue in the Ohakune Carrot Park from the proceeds of the book. Naturally the statue will be in your honour and, once funds have been raised, we can work together on a fun design. I have been in contact with Ollie and he is confident that your fans, the Jollybeans, will buy enough copies to make this dream a reality! I hope to welcome you back to the park in due course for a Grand unveiling.

Best wishes and Happy Birthday!

Dave Scott

Developer of Ohakune Carrot Adventure Park (Carrotland)

14/5/2021.

OHAKUNE CARROT
ADVENTURE PARK TRUST INC.

Peggy Frew | Dave Scott

25

An Unveiling

As sales of the book grew over 2021, it became clear that we would be able to start constructing the statue before the end of the year. When Dave Scott heard we were ready to start construction, he was so happy. At some point in 2022, on a day that will live forever in vegetable history, we got to unveil the new carrot statue at the Ohakune Carrot Adventure Park in New Zealand. I cut the ribbon, everyone clapped and it was the happiest day of my life.

It was a big event for the town of Ohakune, and a huge day for the people of New Zealand who now had another magnificent statue to stand alongside the biggest carrot in the world. It was huge for me too, and really enormous for Ollie, but it was probably hugest for Muncho.

"We owe all this to Ollie," he said, crying tears of joy. "Truly he is the greatest and best friendliest best friend in the world."

"Yes he is," I agreed. "We are truly blessed to know him."

With that, we swanned off together into the sunset.

Acknowledgements

I would like to extend my heartfelt thanks to the many people who helped make this book a reality. Firstly to Adam and Luke for somewhat unbelievably agreeing to let the project go ahead in the first place. To Jordan for your edits and help finding that elusive photo of me interviewing BTS. Thank you to Jenny Lee and Andy Brierley who tirelessly helped me in basically completely re-writing this book from a rather eclectic first draft. I encourage readers to go follow Jenny's instagram @parentsdictionary – it is hilarious and inspiring, just like she is. I owe an enormous debt of gratitude to the multi-talented Ben Thomas for his incredible work on the front cover, having been given a ridiculous and ever-changing brief. To everyone at Compass-Publishing UK, especially Alexa Whitten who guided me through the late-stage rigmarole of typesetting and publication. To Grace, our first ever employee who, true to form, has walked with me on this project from the beginning, and done a stirling job bridging the New Zealand connection. Speaking of which, Dave Scott and the team from Ohakune Carrot Adventure Park are just amazing, and I genuinely feel privileged to have got to know them a little bit over zoom this Spring. I'm really looking forward to meeting you all in person.

Lastly I wish to thank Ollie, my best friend, YouTube co-conspirator and first love. You're the best.

Made in the USA
Middletown, DE
23 March 2022

63106986R00068